Student Workbook & Tool Kit

By Duane Bolin and Luke Holzmann
Edited by Amber Densmer Baker

ISBN: 978-1-935570-02-8

Avyx, Inc.
8032 South Grant Way
Littleton, CO 80122
USA
303-483-0140
www.avyx.com

Table of Contents

Student Workbook

This page intentionally left blank.

Introduction

Student Workbook

Welcome to the MathTacular 4 Workbook!

We created this workbook to accompany the MathTacular 4 DVD. It includes each problem Detective Justin Time and Amber Waves encounter on the DVD, with room on the page for you to try to solve the word problems on your own. When you're finished, you can watch our heroes work through them on the DVD. After each Sample problem in this book, you will find 5 similar Practice Problems that will help you hone your new word problem solving skills.

How to use this workbook with the MathTacular 4 DVD:

In order to understand the MathTacular 4 story, we recommend you begin by watching the first few scenes on the DVD. We'll introduce you to our hero, Detective Justin Time, and the task before him: to assist Amber Waves with her Word Puzzler woes, and eventually rescue her pork-napped pig, Polly Esther.

As each chapter of the story unfolds, our heroes encounter word problems—the same **Sample** word problems found at the beginning of each chapter in this book. Before we solve the problem on the DVD, Detective Time will first ask you to try to solve the problem on your own in your book. Keep in mind that the DVD will stop on its own (unless you've selected "Play All") to give you time to do so. Even if you've never done this type of word problem before, give it your best shot. When you're done, go back to the DVD, press "Continue" and the heroes in our story will walk you through the solution to the word problem.

Once you've solved the Sample problem, Detective Time will give you an opportunity to work on the **Practice Problems** that complete each chapter in this book. Use the skills and techniques you just learned to solve the Sample Problem to tackle each Practice Problem. When you're finished, compare your answers to the answers you'll find in the **Answer Key**. When you're done with all of the additional word problems in a particular section, continue watching the DVD and move on to the next type of word problem—and the next part of the adventure! Can you help Detective Time and Amber Waves solve the mystery?

P.S. Don't forget to check out the handy **Tool Kit** that starts on page 163 to find lists of Clue Words, Units and Measurements and other nuggets that will help you solve the problems in this book.

Note to Parents

Do you remember word problems in math class when you were growing up? Did you love them, or did you sometimes find yourself staring at the page until the words blurred together, wondering where to begin? If only someone had given you a "plan of attack" that worked every time…

Well, that's what we've done here. We hope the instruction in this program will give you and your children the tools you need to overcome Word Problem Intimidation. Take a few minutes to review the Simple Steps to Solve Word Problems on page 166 of the Tool Kit (or on the inside back cover of this book). These steps will teach you how to determine what each problem is asking, and how to pull the relevant information out of that daunting block of words. The more you and your children work through these steps, the more second-nature they will become, and before long, it will seem as though those pesky word problems have finally met their match.

→

Introduction

Student Workbook

We hope the word problem solving doesn't end with the last page of this book. With that goal in mind, we have not limited the "size" and "shape" of these stories to the strict, dry variety you will commonly find in math books. This program gives your children the opportunity to practice these new skills on word problems that may be a little longer, may contain a little extra information, and are guaranteed to be sillier than the ones about Susie and her 5 apples. But through the structured approach, the demonstrations on the DVD, and even the silliness, we gently and intentionally teach your children how to be "comfortable with the hard stuff." This program will give your children the confidence to tackle more complicated word problems than those they will find in any math book.

A Wide Range of Skills: Since we believe that anyone can learn to conquer word problems, we have designed this program to cover a very wide scope of mathematical skills. While there's a good chance that younger students haven't yet studied, say, fractions or ratios in their math curriculum, they will probably still enjoy watching our heroes work through the word problems to find the clues that lead them to Polly Esther, and they may absorb some of the mathematical concepts they'll experience along the way. If you'd like to take it a step further, you can read through the solutions to the tougher problems in the Answer Key, and then see if your children can work out the problem independently. Keep in mind that if you still have many more years of math study in your future, you'll be able to use this program again and again. You'll be able to introduce more of the extra problems in this workbook as your children learn to master new topics in their math curriculum. Whether MathTacular 4 is one of your fun Friday activities or you simply revisit it periodically as you learn new skills in your own math curriculum, we hope this program will become one of your favorite learning tools for years to come.

Final Important Fact About Word Problems: Please remind your children that, regardless of length, most word problems are like newspaper articles—they present the facts. If a word problem didn't specifically give certain information, you probably don't need to know it in order to solve the problem. So, say a problem only gives information about Bernardo belly dancing on Monday, Wednesday and Friday. It's safe to assume, then, that Bernardo did *not* belly dance the rest of the week. Help your children succeed by encouraging them to take these problems at face value.

Calculators? Of course, it is always your choice whether you'd like your children to use a calculator when they're working on mathematical computations. While it's always good "mental exercise" for your children to practice basic math facts, remember that pulling the right information out of a word problem and then correctly building a math problem with that information (that will take you to the *right* answer) is a daunting and complicated task in itself. We encourage you to use this program to first mold the problem solving skills it takes to tackle word problems, and only require calculator-free math when it isn't an added burden. (How much "chicken-scratching" *does* it take to solve $265.30 ÷ 14? Or are you reaching for your calculator too?)

Adding Goats

Simple Addition

Sample Problem

Hannah has four goats. Their names are Loretta, Ignatius, Kimberly, and Bob. Kimberly was Hannah's favorite. Loretta and Bob were the two oldest goats. At the County Fair, Hannah bought three more goats from her friend Amy. These goats are named Tim, Phil, and Wayne. How many goats does she have now?

Practice Problem #1

Simple Addition

Ronald the Raccoon loves to steal garbage from the neighborhood trash cans. On Tuesdays, he visits three trash cans. On Thursdays, he visits six other trash cans. Ronald is considering going out on Saturday night to visit an additional twelve trash cans. If he starts out at 8:00 pm, he figures he can be done by 11:30 pm. If he does go out on Saturday as planned, how many trash cans will Ronald visit altogether each week?

Simple Addition **Practice Problem #2**

Cashew and her brother Samson went fishing down by the Ol' Waterin' Hole. Cashew had her brand new Bezco rod and reel. Samson was using a tuning fork on which he'd tied a piece of string. In the first hour, Cashew landed 27 striped bass, while Samson only managed to wrangle four giant tuna. In the second hour, Cashew caught an additional 12 striped bass, and Samson hauled in 29 Atlantic Salmon. Since they wanted to catch a 3 p.m. matinee of "Aluminum Man," they headed home with their catch. How many fish did they catch in all?

Practice Problem #3

Bo Jest works for "A Clown a Day Keeps the Blues Away" Circus. He was recently promoted from "The Cotton Candy Guy" to "The Guy Who Puts the Clowns in the Tiny Car." Wanting to impress his boss, he promises to fit more clowns into the tiny car than ever before. On his first day, Bo shoves 12 clowns into the tiny car. Then he has an epiphany. After coating the clowns in peanut oil, Bo is able to slide an additional 7 clowns into the car. Still not satisfied, Bo grabs a plunger and a shoe horn and is finally able to squeeze 5 more clowns into the tiny car. How many clowns total did he fit into the tiny car?

Simple Addition

Practice Problem #4

Roger works at a factory and earns $11.27 an hour maintaining the bolt making machine. The machine has a maximum output capacity of 225 bolts per day. Unfortunately, it breaks down often. On Monday the machine was able to spit out 217 bolts before falling apart. It took Roger until the factory closed on Thursday night to get the machine up and running again. On Friday the machine made another 192 bolts before it completely fell apart. How many bolts did the machine manage to make that week?

Practice Problem #5

Simple Addition

It was lab day at the Practicum for Underwater Terrestrial Research of Invertebrate Digestion: P.U.T.R.I.D. Sandy, Sunny, and Al were in a group. Sandy's tapeworm had collected 0.03 L of digestive fluid. Sunny was only able to extract 0.16 L of digestive fluid from his starfish. And Al's three-pound Grouper had a shockingly low level of liquid with only 0.59 L. The lab sheet asked: How many Liters of digestive fluid are there in your three specimens altogether? What should the lab partners write down as their answer?

Careful! There is only one significant question to answer here.

Dagmar Olsen loves flapjacks. Yesterday, he ate 17 flapjacks for breakfast. Mysteriously, Dagmar's tummy started to ache shortly thereafter. He went to the doctor, and the nurse told him he was 47 inches tall and weighed 273 pounds. Yesterday, Dagmar's best friend, Elton Noberto, ate 3 bowls of "You Can't Beat Wheat" cereal. Later that day, Elton went to the doctor for a check-up. The nurse told him he was 61 inches tall and weighed 126 pounds less than Dagmar Olsen. How much does Elton Norberto weigh?

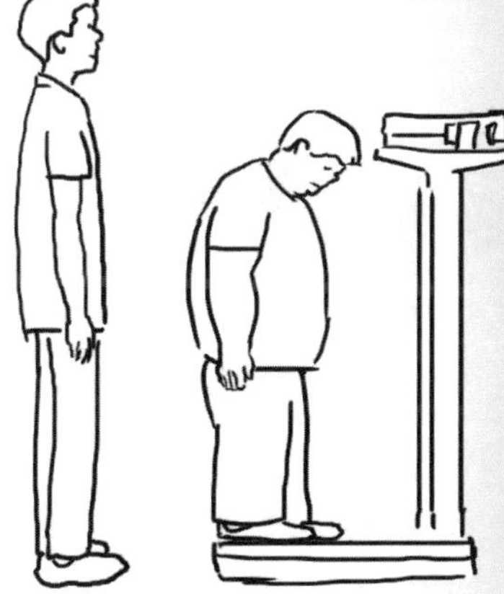

2 Practice Problem #1

Simple Subtraction

Custer and Buster were very competitive twin hedgehogs. One fine Saturday, they agreed to saddle up their horses and compete to see who could ride the farthest that day. At the crack of 10 a.m., Buster broke out to an early lead and soon left Custer in the dust. At Tuna Fork, Buster took the High Road and kept his lightning-quick pace. When Custer reached the Fork, he could see from the tracks in the dust that the only chance he'd have would be to go down the Low Road. When night fell, Buster had traveled an amazing 293 miles. Due to an unfortunate incident at Little Bighorn, Custer ended up traveling 154 miles less than Buster that day. How many miles did Custer travel that fateful Saturday?

Iglopuk, an Inuit entrepreneur from Gnome, Alaska, took a cab from the Miami airport to the Everglades. When he jumped in the cab, it was a blazing 98 degrees inside! The cabbie apologized for the heat but confessed that his air conditioner had been broken for a week. Without skipping a beat, Iglopuk opened his bag and flipped on the air conditioner he'd made out of an old VCR, baling wire and a used A/B switch. By the time the cab reached the Everglades, it was 32 degrees cooler inside the cab than it had been at the airport. What temperature was it inside the cab when they got to the Everglades?

2 Practice Problem #3

Nevil the Rat knows that there are 37 treats on the third shelf of the bookcase. As a sensible rat, he loves treats, food, and just about anything he can put in his mouth and digest. After three days of failed attempts, he is finally able to get to the third shelf by climbing up the pile of laundry to the chair, the chair to the windowsill, and, with nothing more than a dangerous lateral leap, to the shelf and his prize. Hungry from his climb, Nevil promptly consumes 18 of the treats until he is discovered, scolded and put back in his cage. How many treats are left for Nevil's next excursion?

Granny and Fanny were the lone contestants in the final round of the Ultimate Speed Knitting Championship. At the bell, their needles clicked and whirred into a blur—some even thought they saw smoke rising from Granny's hands! The match was expected to be close, but unfortunately, Fanny's patented Yarn Unwinder 5000 jammed in the final seconds and Granny blew past her to the finish. Final scarf measurements confirmed that Granny had knit an astonishing 163 feet, while Fanny had only knit 124 feet. How much longer was Granny's championship-winning scarf?

2 Practice Problem #5

It was an unusually dark and stormy night. In fact, Luke could not remember the last time the annual Ocho de Mayo celebration had been rained out. As he wandered home, his mind went back to '88, when he was crowned King Burrito. He had put away 60 burritos in only 30 minutes that year. In '89 he had eaten 12 fewer burritos, but he had also just recovered from a serious bout with rickets—just enough of a handicap to allow Miz Chalupa to steal his crown. Finally, in '90, he once again reigned supreme…Burrito Supreme, that is. That year, Miz Chalupa could only gulp down 10 fewer burritos than Luke had the previous year. Since that time, Luke's reign earned him the nickname "Ol' Iron Stomach." How many burritos did Miz Chalupa eat in '90?

Trail Mix

Addition / Subtraction Two-Step Problems

Sample Problem

3

A beaver and an otter were creating a trail from the beaver's dam to the otter's apartment. The beaver was 7 years old and the otter was almost 12. The first morning, they were able to blaze a trail 62 feet long. That afternoon, it rained so they took the rest of the day off, as well as the next morning. The next afternoon, the otter and the beaver created 17 fewer feet of new trail than they had the previous morning. How many feet of trail did the beaver and the otter create on that afternoon? How many feet of trail did they finish in total?

Trail Mix

Practice Problem #1

3

Rolando Fitzgerald was arguably the most handsome brother of the circus act, The Famous Five Fitzgeralds. Seriously, neither Orlando nor Lorando nor Randolfo could hold a candle to his rugged good looks. Only his youngest brother, Pete, had the same flowing locks and golden skin tone that made the lasses swoon. Rolando also stood an impressive 195 cm tall. Pete, on the other hand, was 45 cm shorter. However, Pete knew that his height was particularly suited to jumping. He could spring into the air, turn somersaults, and land on the head of a pin…or, occasionally, the head of a brother. Pete once sprang into the air, did a double back flip, and landed squarely on the freshly-combed locks of Rolando. With Pete standing on Rolando's head, what was the total height of the two brothers?

Trail Mix

Addition/Subtraction Two-Step Problems

Practice Problem #2

The competition was stiff at this year's Merry Men (and Women) Marksmanship Tryouts for the local Renaissance Fair. Each contestant shoots 5 arrows at a target. A bull's-eye is worth 10 points, which means it is possible to score a maximum of 50 points. Ms. Marion's first three arrows scored a 7, a 6 and a 6. For her last two arrows, she readjusted her stance, tightened the bow stabilizer and scored an 8 and a 9. What is the difference between the points Ms. Marion scored and the total points possible?

Practice Problem #3

Gillian loves to play with the hose. She loves to fill up buckets and dump them out so she can fill them up again. Gillian's new green bucket can hold 6 gallons. She also has a one-gallon milk jug and a two-gallon detergent bottle. If Gillian emptied both the milk jug and the detergent bottle into her green bucket, how much water would be in the bucket? How much more water would Gillian need to pour into her bucket if she wanted to fill it to the brim?

Trail Mix

Addition / Subtraction Two-Step Problems

Practice Problem #4

3

Earl has wanted an Atlantic Coast Limited Edition 2% Sharkskin Full-Body swimsuit for years. Unfortunately, the cost is a little outside of his price range. Exactly \$3.27 outside, in fact. So of course Earl was excited when Atlantic Coast offered a \$3.59 mail-in rebate. Since stamps still cost only \$0.32 at that time, the suit was finally within his budget. If the normal price for the suit is \$302.99, how much money will Earl spend, factoring in the cost of the stamp?

Practice Problem #5

Dave E. Jones, the one-eyed fish, thought his chances were pretty good for winning the Moat Mile. The first fish to successfully complete 12 laps around the castle's moat would win. Since the tragic welding accident, Dave E. swam in circles so he could keep an eye on everything around him—and he thought these spins would lead him to an easy victory. Of course, all of the other fish believed his circular reasoning was somewhat faulty. Nonetheless, Dave E. stepped up his training regimen so that he now practices 3 days per week. He swam an astounding 100 laps during practice on Monday. On Wednesday, he swam 12 fewer laps than on Monday. On Friday, he swam 7 fewer laps than he had on Wednesday. How many total laps did he swim this week?

Simple Multiplication

Sample Problem

Chef Justin Time fixed three bowls of fresh fruit for his friend Amber Waves. In each bowl, he put three pieces of fruit: three apples in the first bowl, three oranges in the second bowl, and three bananas in the third bowl. How many pieces of fruit are there in all?

Practice Problem #1

Simple Multiplication

As Oscar was about to jump off of a particularly large tree root, he noticed a very old bottle. Rubbing the side of the bottle to remove the dirt on the label, Oscar was shocked to see a note pop out of the top of the bottle, which read: "Bearer of this note entitled to three wishes. Wishes for more wishes are not allowed. Void where prohibited. Results may vary." After a bit of thought, he decided that his first wish would be—not for more wishes, *exactly*—but to find more bottles just like the one he had just found. Feeling smug at his brilliance, Oscar started home. Along the way, he found 7 more bottles, each with a note entitling the finder to three wishes. How many wishes total did Oscar earn today?

Simple Multiplication

Practice Problem #2

Mr. Sutton, the beloved math teacher at Little Quirky High School, is very particular. Every Monday is Spirit Day, and every Spirit Day, Mr. Sutton wears his bright blue pants. Also, Mr. Sutton coaches the school's pickleball team that plays on Wednesdays, so every Wednesday, he again wears the blue pants. Therefore, on Sundays and Tuesdays each week, Mrs. Sutton runs a load of laundry to make sure the favorite blue pants are ready for the upcoming event. If today is September 1st, how many times will Mrs. Sutton wash the blue pants in the 16 weeks before Christmas Break begins?

Practice Problem #3

Simple Multiplication

4

After being duly sworn in as the new President of the Board of Shady Acres Convalescent Retreat, Old Man Jenkins made good on his campaign promise to provide all guests with a goodie bag of treats. He decided each goodie bag would contain 1 toothbrush, 5 tea bags, 2 decks of cards, 1 jar of Bran Nuggets, 1 pair of trifocals, and a collapsible cane to keep the young whippersnappers in line. After five hours of work, two naps, and a trip to China Buffet for the Early Bird Special, Old Man Jenkins had assembled 87 goodie bags for the residents of Shady Acres. How many tea bags did he use?

Simple Multiplication

Practice Problem #4

Tayler loves to help in the nursery at church. Every Sunday, Tayler has helped watch Zoé, Camden, Brandon and Madison. Each baby plays with three toys each week, and each week when the children go home, Tayler washes all of the toys and puts them away. How many toys has Tayler washed in the past four weeks?

Practice Problem #5

Simple Multiplication

On Friday nights, Kevin and his friends spend their evening at Ted and Harry's Arcade. This week Kevin was busy mowing lawns, so he arrives at the arcade with $10.00 to spend. Kevin's favorite game is Bowler Ball because he can win 8 tickets for each game he plays. If every Bowler Ball game costs $0.50, how much money will he spend to play 9 games? Does he have enough money to play 9 games?

Split the Bill

Simple Division

Sample Problem

At last month's Metropolis Detectives' Association meeting, 8 detectives ate Beef Fajitas (not Pork Rind Casserole). The recipe called for 4 pounds of beef, 4 green peppers, 2 large onions, and 16 flour tortillas. The total for the ingredients was $16. The detectives split the cost of the groceries evenly. How much did each detective pay?

Split the Bill

Practice Problem #1

Simple Division

Kelly left her weekly Snickerdoodle troop meeting clutching the cookie order form. She had big plans. Her heart was set on going to Camp Pinecone again this year. Last year, she had met her best friend, Valorie, there, and the two had spent a blissful week building hummingbird feeders, learning to weave baskets underwater, and making up silly songs until all hours of the night. Her troop leader had told Kelly that if she could sell 270 cookies, she'd earn the troop's scholarship and wouldn't have to pay the usual $175 for the trip. If each box contains 18 cookies, how many boxes will Kelly need to sell to win the scholarship?

Old Man Jenkins wanted to split his fortune evenly amongst his 42 descendants. And that was no easy task, for his fortune amounted to a whopping $1,915,200. It was a testament to clipping coupons and avoiding infomercials about salad spinners and grills named after that famous rollerpolo player. If you were one of Old Man Jenkins' descendants, how much would you stand to inherit if he suddenly met his demise?

Practice Problem #3

Delbert emerged from Swanson's Corner Truck Stop grinning like a 5 year old on his birthday. He plopped back into the driver's seat and revealed the bag of 100 licorice ropes he'd purchased inside. Mama gave him a look of reproach as he started dividing the ropes evenly among his cheering fan base—the five kids in the back seat. Knowing that the older kids, Delbert Jr., Katarina, Isabella and Norm, could pace themselves, Mama started to worry that Delbert would spoil the baby's dinner with his little treat. How many licorice ropes did Delbert give to baby Maude?

Bubbly Betty and her band of bodacious balloon bursters bopped onto the grounds of the biggest Balloon Bashing Bout since '56. The bunch of beauties had been training biweekly for months, and now quietly eyed the Big Bad Boomer trophy with humble admiration. They knew that they'd need to be at the top of their game if they stood a chance to win the competition. In order for Betty's band to beat the best time, each of the 4 team members would need to burst an equal share of the competition-sized balloon bouquet. When their match began, Betty's bunch was blown away when they realized that their balloon bundle held an unprecedented 256 balloons. How many balloons should each balloon burster bash?

Practice Problem #5

Simple Division

5

Leon looked about and then popped a stray jelly bean into his mouth. As much fun as looking for eggs in the town's yearly Egg Hunt had been a few years ago, he'd recently taken a shine to helping the adults get everything ready the night before—mostly because Mrs. Waddlekins (the Egg Hunt Head Honcho) told him he could snack on as much of the leftover candy as he wanted. His current task is to evenly separate a fresh bag of 192 jellybeans into two dozen plastic eggs. When Leon completes his task, how many jelly beans will each plastic egg hold?

Donut Dilemma

Old Man Jenkins bought 7 boxes of Squish Custard donuts at the Inconvenience Store. He paid $35.99 for the donuts, which he thought was way too much for an old man on a fixed income. There were 13 donuts in each box. If Mr. Jenkins gives one donut to each person at Shady Acres, how many people will get a free donut?

Old Man Jenkins needed to take a 3-hour nap after carrying the donuts. If the total weight of the donuts was 728 grams and each donut was the same weight, how much did each donut weigh?

Practice Problem #1

Multiplication / Division Two-Step Problems

Dolly the Llama loved mashed potatoes. At exactly 6:23 a.m. every day, her human, Farmer Kip, would fill up his wagon with 56 pounds of potatoes and bring them to the barn where his 4 children would divide them into 7 equal piles. Then, Farmer Kip's wife, Linda, would take 2 piles of potatoes and mash them up with butter and garlic for Dolly's breakfast. How many pounds of mashed potatoes does Dolly the Llama eat for breakfast each morning?

Donut Dilemma

Practice Problem #2

Sadly, twelve years of drought had left Jackrabbit Hill parched. In the glory days, rabbits would've spent all day guiding their canoes and kayaks down Jackrabbit Hill's many waterways. Over the last dozen years, though, the rabbits could only hike their way down the 8 dry creek beds that wound their way from the summit to the base of the hill. But that would all change today. Chugging along up the side of the hill were 4 tanker trucks, each filled with 1,250 gallons of water. The rabbits' plan was to erect a giant water tower, fill it with the water from the trucks, and then release the water into the creeks. If the rabbits divide the water equally between the creeks, how many gallons of water will each creek have?

Donut Dilemma

Chris Gibson opened the door and took a deep breath of the fresh sparkling air. Ah, Spring. Today was the opening day of his Sherwood Forest Petting Zoo. He turned on his heel and decided it was time to wake the critters. Since the weather had been so warm yesterday, he'd asked his new assistant, Marty, to put two of the new water bowls he'd ordered last week in each of the seven cages. Well, the new water bowls looked fine and dandy, but after a moment's observation, Chris decided that the newness of the water bowls made the food bowls look particularly slobbery and shabby. As he sauntered back to his office, he remembered that the Woodland Creature Supply Company also offered food bowls that were the same price as water bowls, and that he had paid $265.30 for the new bowls. What price did Chris Gibson pay per bowl for the new set of water bowls?

Hint: How many water bowls did Marty leave in the cages yesterday?

Donut Dilemma

Multiplication / Division Two-Step Problems

Practice Problem #4

The incident was as unfortunate as unfortunate incidents can come. Along his daily roll, Old Man Jenkins somehow managed to high-center his All-Terrain Motor Seat 3000 on an unusually large stone. But that wasn't the worst of it. After dismounting to assess the situation, he then proceeded to snap his only cane in two while trying to pry said stone from beneath the Motor Seat. Now, seat-less, cane-less, and frustrated as all get-out, Old Man Jenkins had to hobble down to Canes R Us to see about replacing his third cane that month. He finally settled on a 3-foot model with a mother-of-pearl handle, but again left the store empty-handed when the clerk told him the cane cost $185! He wobbled home and eventually found the exact same cane on eBuy for $135. Still skeptical about the price, he did a little cipherin' and discovered that the price per inch of the eBuy cane still wasn't a great deal. How much did the eBuy cane cost per inch?

Hint: How many inches are in each foot?

Donut Dilemma

The ants of Grassy Knoll had foraged well that summer. Matilda, the queen ant, sat back one late summer afternoon and surveyed their winter stock piles. According to the accounting department, each of the 4 foraging battalions had contributed 37,829,996 morsels of food to the storehouses that season. Knowing it was time to divert workers to prepare the hill for winter, Matilda glanced again over the current roster and found there were 2,789 ants currently living in the hill. If Matilda stopped all foraging efforts now and divided the stored food evenly between the ants, how many morsels of food would each ant have to eat that winter?

Bubba is the Official Fill-Up Man at the local FASCAR track. On race day, he leaves home at 7:00 a.m. and arrives at the FASCAR track at 7:37 a.m. Bubba's tank has 247 liters of high-quality FASCAR fuel.

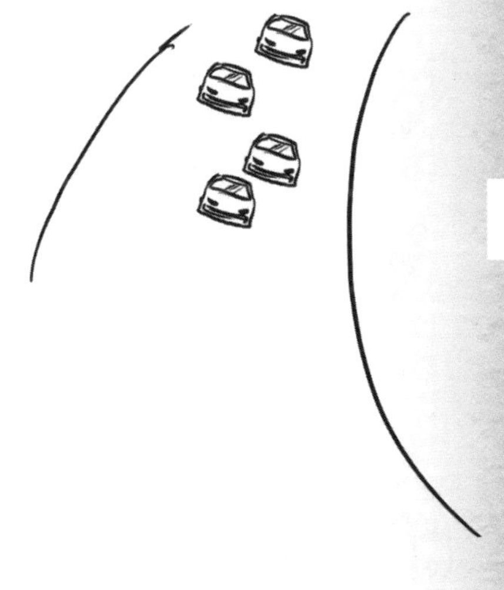

Halfway through the race, Gordon Jeffers pulls his car up to Bubba's tank for a fill-up. He is followed by Ernie Dalehard, Stewart Tonay and John Jimmyson. Each driver requests 70 liters of gas, but Bubba does not have that much gas! Bubba divides the gas evenly between the four drivers. Gordon Jeffers eventually wins in a photo finish. How much gas did Bubba pass to each of the four drivers? How much gas did he have left at the end of the day?

Practice Problem #1

Times were rough on the high seas for the dread pirate Plaidbeard. His old crew had dipped a little too freely into the buried treasure when that new-fangled iPaddle hit the market, and now they all spent their days rowing about the harbor in their little skiffs, and generally not doing anything. Now, strapped for cash, Plaidbeard was forced to hire the cheapest labor he could find—14 landlubbers who clearly had left their sea legs back on the dock. And therein lay Plaidbeard's dilemma: Each scurvy knave needed 3 seasickness pills, but Plaidbeard had only purchased a small generic bottle of seasickness medication with 30 pills in it—not enough to give each sick crew member a full dose. Deciding that a partial dose was better than nothing, Plaidbeard divides the pills evenly amongst his crew. How many pills does each crew member get? How many pills will be left over?

Captain Johan Beagleman pulled his convoy of wagons to a halt at a crossroads in Inner Mongolia. There were 22 wagons in his convoy carrying a variety of meats, cheeses, spices and pre-owned auto parts. The road ahead split into 4 different paths. But which one would lead them to riches of the Lost City of Pyrite? There was no way to be sure of the right path, and yet it was just as dangerous to wait at the crossroads with their goods for scouting parties to return with information. What if a wild pack of former vegetarians got a craving for Inner Mongolian BBQ? Praying that he was making the right decision, Beagleman grabbed his bullhorn and announced that he would send an equal number of wagons down each trail, leaving the fewest number of wagons to guard the goods. How many wagons would go down each trail? How many would remain to protect their goods?

Practice Problem #3

Marjorie was proud of her efforts to date. With a lot of hard work, she'd been able to secure 40 local donors to kick-start her Save the Owls campaign. She had promised the local donors that, should she secure a national sponsor, she would return to each of them an equal portion of the money, while using whatever was left over to build an owl sanctuary on the roof of the local Smoothie Joint. Impressed by Marjorie's campaign, the Onomatopoeia Wouldn'twannabeya League of Superheroes (O.W.L.S.) donated $2,190 in Susan B. Anthony coins as the first national sponsor of Marjorie's campaign. True to her word, she split the coins equally amongst the local supporters. If each coin is worth $1, how much did each supporter receive? How many coins were left over for the rooftop owl sanctuary?

Quotient and Remainder

Practice Problem #4

Vladimir Eclair scratched his head. Dear, sweet Mrs. Witt had hired him to build a picket fence around her prized petunia patch, but had insisted that she order the pickets herself from her son's woodworking company. In hopes of avoiding mishap, he had tried to be very clear that he would need 3 pickets per foot of fence she'd like him to build. And while she had sounded confident at the time, he was baffled when her son's company later delivered only 23 pickets. How many whole feet of fence is Vladimir Eclair able to build? How many pickets were left over?

Practice Problem #5

Quotient and Remainder

Juan Pablo sighed. Due to a shocking rock-paper-scissors upset, he now had Albino Duck duty—his least favorite job at the nature preserve. Not only did the 173 ducks tend to be complaining prima donnas, it was also the height of summer which meant he had to coat every one of them with a generous dollop of duck lotion—Duck Protection Factor 300—to keep their sensitive skin from frying and creating one massive order of Duck L'Orange. As Juan Pablo grabbed a tub of lotion tubes, he realized there were only 513 small tubes of lotion left. If he coats each duck equally, how many tubes of duck lotion will each duck receive? How many tubes will be left over?

Babs Anchorpants loves to swim. Her favorite swimmin' hole is Porcupine Pond. Each morning at 6:00 a.m., Babs throws herself into the pond and swims 12 laps as fast as she can. Each lap is 10 yards long. Unfortunately for Babs, she swims really…really…slow. It takes Babs 1 hour to complete her workout. At 7:00 a.m. Babs' arch-nemesis, Bubbles McGee, shows up. Bubbles says she can swim faster than Babs. Babs says, "Prove it, Bubbles!" Bubbles dives in and when all is said and swam, Bubbles completed 12 laps in 1/5 of the time it took Babs. How long did it take Bubbles to swim 12 laps in Porcupine Pond? How much longer did it take Babs to swim those dozen laps?

Practice Problem #1

Stanley the Singing Frog tossed the end of his scarf over his shoulder, picked up the microphone and began to belt out an a cappella version of "It Ain't Easy Being Green." Tonight's show at La Cantina Loco was the final show of the year. As he looked back over the past 365 days, Stanley could scarcely believe this was his 300th performance of the year. Stanley's stage stamina was the envy of all the other singing animal performers, including Rice & Beans, the singing mouse duo from Monterrey.
As hard as they had tried, Rice & Beans had been able to perform only two-thirds the number of shows Stanley had over the course of the previous year. How many shows had Rice & Beans performed?

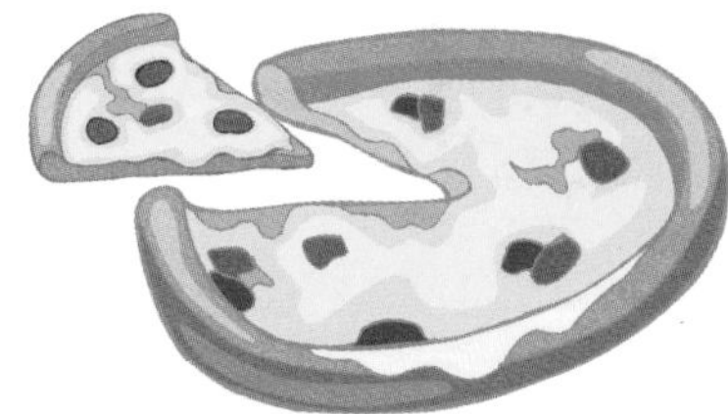

The clock struck 11 p.m. and Biff and Squash suddenly realized they were famished. Even though they had arrived for dinner in the dorm cafeteria promptly at 6:07 p.m., their meal of mystery meat and mushy peas just wasn't going to make it for that long night of presentation preparation ahead of them. Now, after 28 minutes of sheer anticipation (and excavating a spot in the teenage-boy-carnage on the dorm room floor), the two sat with a Cheese Monster pizza between them, lovingly cut into 12 equal slices. Unfortunately, they soon realized that their eyes had been bigger than their stomachs. While Biff did manage to eat 1/3 of the pizza, Squash could only put away 1/4 of it. How many pieces did each lad eat?

Practice Problem #3

Percival the otter loved clams. So when he stumbled across a rickety shack in a forgotten part of the wharf with a sign that read "Bucket of Clams—$5," he thought he'd struck gold. After seating himself at a small table and placing his order, Babs, the waitress, heaved the most enormous bucket of clams he'd ever seen onto his table. Babs noticed the otter's eyes bulge as she did so, and informed Percival that each bucket held 175 clams. Undaunted, Percival flipped onto his back, pulled his trusty pet rock out of his pocket and began to crack open the clams on his stomach. After giving it his best effort, Percival finally gave up when he'd finished 4/5 of the clams. How many clams did Percival eat?

Fractions

Practice Problem #4

Gracie stared out the window, daydreaming as she watched the last student skip to her car after dress rehearsal. Her young swans were only 1 day away from their debut performance of "People Lake" and she knew it was simply going to be the best ballet performance the swans on this side of the pond had ever seen. She hoped that all of the money she had spent sponsoring this year's event would translate into a packed house for tomorrow night's show. Gracie figured that, of the 80 available seats, 5/8 of them would need to be filled in order for her to break even. How many seats need to be filled at tomorrow night's performance for Gracie's production to break even?

Practice Problem #5

Polly Popsicle, owner of the Fabulous Frozen Treats Company looked over the results from that year's springtime treat survey. As it had been a surprisingly warm spring, she had received a whopping 320 responses to her "My Top Treat" survey. One quarter of the respondents had selected Frosted Gooeys as their treat of choice while 5/16 preferred the Icy Sours. The remaining 7/16 of those surveyed had voted for Crunchy Gum Gum Yummers as their favorite snack—which explained why Yummers sales had spiked in the last month. How many votes did each treat receive?

A Walk Around the Cement Pond

Perimeter **Sample Problem**

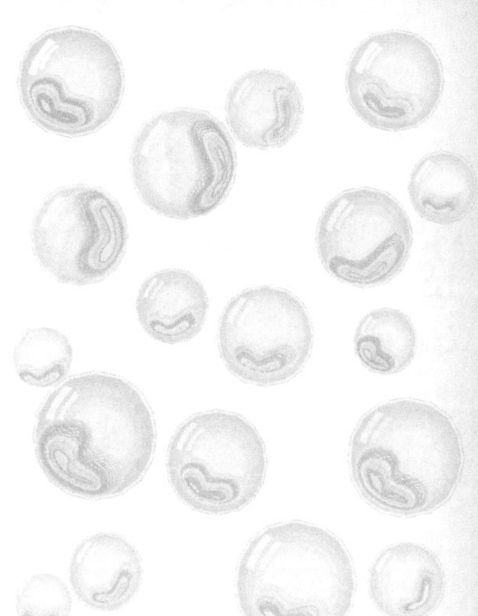

Bubbles McGee loves to swim at the cement pond of Muddy Waters. It is a large rectangle that is 100 meters long and 50 meters wide. Bubbles invites Babs Anchorpants to a swimming party at the pond. But Bubbles' invitation was a ruse to lure Babs into another competition. Bubbles says that she can swim to the other side of the pond and back faster than Babs can walk around it.

9

Bubbles' best friend, Wanda, starts the race. Unbeknownst to Bubbles, Babs walks much faster than she swims. Although Bubbles took only 2 minutes to swim, Babs walked around the pond in 5/9 of that time. How far did Babs walk on her trip around the cement pond?

Perimeter = l + l + w + w

OR

Perimeter = 2(l) + 2(w)

Hint: Sometimes it helps to label a picture with information you know.

Practice Problem #1

Perimeter

9

The Sicilian Lovers of Oregon Pizzassociation (S.L.O.P.) were holding their 30th biannual fundraiser. However, this year, the stakes were high. If every one of their 348 members did not sell at least 83 jars of pizza sauce, their grand plans to build the world's largest Sicilian pizza would never be realized. The pizza would be the size of a football field: 360 feet long by 160 feet wide. A pizza that size would need truck-loads of toppings, and a thick crust to go all the way around each of its four sides. Assuming the fundraiser is successful and the members of S.L.O.P are able to build their dream pizza, how many feet of crust will they need to frame their edible work of art?

Clem just had to win the Square Dance competition this year. He simply could not face the prospect of being runner-up for the 4th year in a row. So he decided to turn his garage into a home studio where he could practice to his heart's content. To figure out how much wood he'd need to construct a dance floor, he knew he would need to measure his garage. With his trusty meter stick, he measured the first wall and found it was 32 meters long. But when he measured each of the other walls, the strangest thing happened. Each wall measured the same as the first! His garage was a true square! Could anything be more perfect for square dancing? In his excitement, he danced a jig along all four walls of the garage. How many meters did Clem jig in his excitement?

A Walk Around the Cement Pond

Practice Problem #3

Perimeter

9

The cattle wranglers were exhausted. Yet one of them would have to keep watch. It wasn't fair, of course, that they had been working since sun-up to retrieve the dozen cows that had managed to escape from the ranch. Luckily, they had stumbled across three sections of fence abandoned on the prairie. The longest section was 65 feet long. The other two sections were both 60 feet. Racing to beat dusk, the wranglers used the fence sections to create a triangular pen for the wayward cattle. Now the youngest, Joe Bob, had been chosen to take the first watch. To help keep his eyes open, Joe Bob decided to walk around and around the cow's pen. How many feet will Joe Bob walk each time he walks all the way around the triangular pen?

Half of the kids on the playground wanted to play Department of Defense. The other half, however, wanted to play Duck, Duck, Goose. As class president, Mildred suggested that they should use some old boards to construct a pentagon-shaped clubhouse for the Department of Defense, and the Duck, Duck, Goose crowd could play around the outside of the clubhouse. Since everyone thought this was a grand compromise, Joey Badabing found five large boards. One measured 16 feet long. Two others were exactly 23 feet long. The last two were 17 feet and 18 feet long, respectively. As soon as they had arranged the boards into a rough pentagon for the clubhouse, the rest of the kids began to run around the clubhouse, shouting "Duck!"… "Duck!"… "Goose!" How many feet did the children run each time they went around the clubhouse?

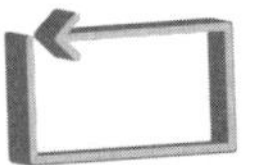

A Walk Around the Cement Pond

Practice Problem #5

Perimeter

9

King Bubbaloo was always concerned about security. Several years ago, he worried that the 50-ft. high stone walls would not be enough to protect the kingdom if they were attacked. So all of his subjects banded together to build a rectangular moat around the castle that was 150 yards long and 100 yards wide. After years of hard labor, the moat was finally finished and filled with water from the local spring. To celebrate, King Bubbaloo allowed the workers to swim in the moat—which turned out to be so much fun that King Bubbaloo added a couple of slides and turned his prized defense mechanism into a waterpark. Every year now, King Bubbaloo holds a Swimming of the Moat race to encourage his subjects to stay physically fit. To complete one lap around the moat, how far must one swim?

Bits and Pieces

Juan and Wanda grabbed all of their allowance money and headed off to The Pawn Shop. Juan saw an electric guitar that was $60.00, but he did not have enough money to buy it. Wanda found an electric waffle maker that was on sale for only $5.00. They shopped until 11:00 a.m. and then they went next door to have lunch at The Prawn Shop. Juan had a Big Prawn sandwich, and Wanda had Prawn Nuggets. Since Juan had bought Wanda's lunch last Thursday, Wanda paid for both of their lunches today. After lunch, they headed back to The Pawn Shop, where Juan ended up spending 3/5 of his money on barbecue tongs that cost $30.00. How much money did Juan have to start with?

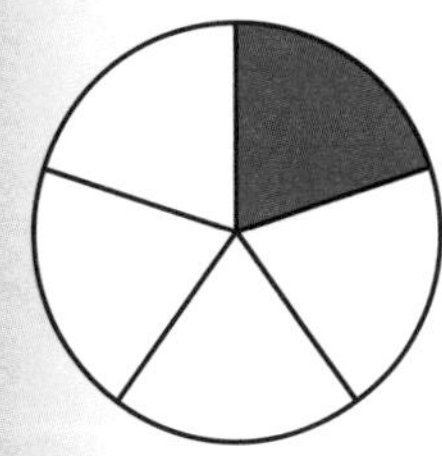

Hint: If you can figure out what one piece of the "pie" is worth, how can you use that information to find the value of the whole pie?

Practice Problem #1

The day broke bright and sunny. Esteban was smiling at 6 a.m. as his feet hit the floor, ready to start a new day. Yesterday had been rough. The Sisters of Infinite Mercy had worked him hard all day long, but today he would have some free time, and he began to wonder what he should do with it. That new "Tae Kwan Do Tiger" movie was out, but of course, his miniature golf game could use some work, too. He decided to mull over the options while he fixed the weight bench at the convent. Five hours later, the Sisters of Infinite Mercy were again pumping iron and Esteban headed to the theater. Unfortunately, the movie was sold out, so he ended up spending 2/3 of his free time watching a 120-minute documentary about Alpaca farming in the Andes. In all, how much free time did Esteban have that day?

Fraction Two-Step Problems

Practice Problem #2

Delores was fed up. She slammed the trunk and jumped in the driver's seat. Although it was already 5:30 p.m., she knew if she kept the pedal to the metal she could make Phuntown by sundown. Anything was better than Littletown, but really, Megalopolis was her final destination. After a stop for several bites to eat at Phuntown's More Than You Should Eat Buffet, Delores decided to turn in so she could start early in the morning. The next day, Delores drove the final 500 miles to the big city, which was 4/5 of the distance between Littletown and Megalopolis. However, upon her arrival, she realized she'd made a huge mistake: what opportunity was there for a professional shepherdess in the big city? She vowed to drive straight home to Littletown the next morning. How many miles in total will Dolores drive to return home to Littletown from Megalopolis?

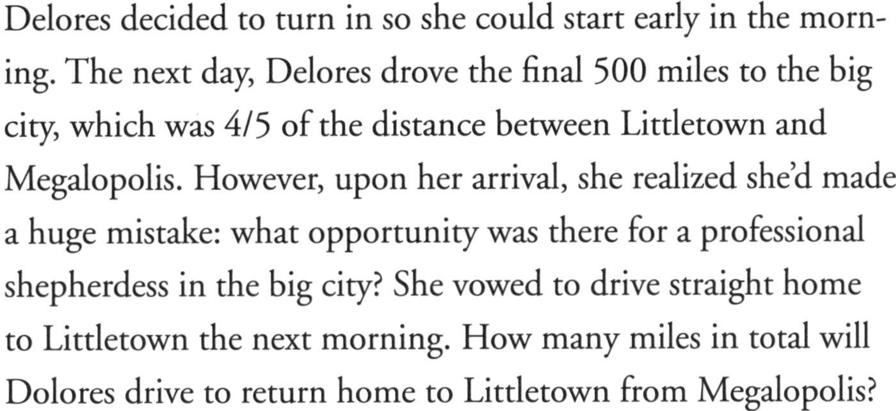

Practice Problem #3

Norm's first experience with his new Scrubadub Whirlyjet Tub hadn't gone well. He'd filled it to the brim with scalding hot water, and even though the temperature caused him to leap back out again at lightning speed, it wasn't before his body mass had displaced a significant portion of water…which leaked through poor Mrs. Kaplansky's ceiling, right in the middle of "Squeal or No Squeal." And yes, she squealed. But Norm had changed a few things since then. He had to, as the Scrubadub Whirlyjet Tub is the only device known to man that could remove the muck that Norm accumulated on his body as a mechanic at the local Quickky Lube. He now filled the tub with 40 gallons of significantly-cooler water, which filled the tub only 5/8 of the way to capacity. What is the total capacity of Norm's Scrubadub Whirlyjet Tub?

Fraction Two-Step Problems

Practice Problem #4

Bubba wanted to do something special for his rollerpolo team. Not only had the Holy Rollers completely turned their season around, they had finally beaten their rivals, the Rusty Buckets, in the championship game. Now, here they sat, basking in the glory of very small trophies and a medium-sized cash prize. Counting the money, Bubba decided to order $25 worth of pizza to celebrate. After their bellies were full, Bubba figured he'd better use the remaining funds to restock the first aid supplies. If Bubba had spent 5/6 of the money on pizza, how much money did he have to start with?

Practice Problem #5

Archibald sighed. Once again, Joan—the enormous sow who was new to the farm—beat him to the slop. Even though Archibald was a gentleman and more than happy to let ladies go first, most ladies didn't throw their weight around the barnyard, demanding to be called "Joan of Pork." And they certainly didn't eat 45 pounds of slop in a sitting the way Joan did—5/16 of the total slop available, and way more than her fair share. Even though the Farm Arbitration Team (F.A.T.) once confronted Joan about her inconsiderate eating habits, Joan continued in her selfish ways. On a typical day, how many pounds of slop in total did the pigs have to share?

Otar-Lina and Brakabrik are foreign exchange students from the Republic of Yoothmanistan. Their homeland is 3,047 miles away from where they are staying in Denver, Colorado, USA. Their favorite sport from their homeland is called Whammyball. The relatively-unknown game is played on a rectangular field. In their homeland, there is a brand new Whammyball stadium, the floor of which measures 120.5 yards by 80.2 yards. The field is regulation size and lies within the stadium floor, with a 10.7 yard margin all around it. Brakabrik's favorite Whammyball team won the championship last year by a score of 456.8 to 379.2. What is the area of a regulation Whammyball field?

Area = l x w

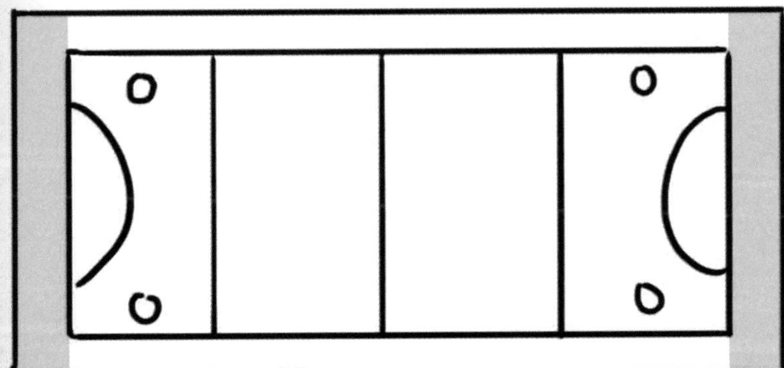

Field of Dreams

Practice Problem #1

Perimeter/Area Two-Step Problems

Presentation was so critical. How many times had Chef Legume told his students that? But in this week's competition, it appeared someone had finally listened. Sauntering over to a beautifully formed Molten Brownie Diet-Destroyer on a bone-white plate, Chef Legume beamed. The plate measured 20 cm by 30 cm, which left a tasteful 2.5 cm margin between the edge of the plate and the side of chocolatey bliss. With his mind made up that this dish had earned the Fuchsia Ribbon, Chef Legume turned over the name card and was shocked to find that Larry, the brash American who insisted upon deep frying everything was responsible for this week's winning entry. What was the total area of Larry's brownie creation?

Field of Dreams

Perimeter/Area Two-Step Problems

Practice Problem #2

Lanky Linda tugged on the sheet again, only to pull the top part away from the headboard. How could this be? She and her mother had made a special trip to Crates and Cribs just before she came back to college and had carefully purchased sheets for her enormous new bed. Then, like a water-filled sponge, it struck her: she must have grabbed her little sister's new sheets by mistake! No wonder when she laid the flat sheet out on her bed, there was a half-meter margin on each side. If Linda's bed measures 6 meters by 4 meters, what was the area of her little sister's sheet?

Practice Problem #3

Rowland handed his picture to the kid behind the counter at Frames Galore. After a moment's contemplation, he opted for the deluxe framing package, thinking to himself, "If I'm going to be framed, I might as well get the deluxe treatment." Rowland knew his picture measured 4 inches by 6 inches, and that the deluxe package included a one-inch mat that would add an inch on each side of the picture. What is the area of Rowland's matted picture?

Field of Dreams

Perimeter/Area Two-Step Problems

Practice Problem #4

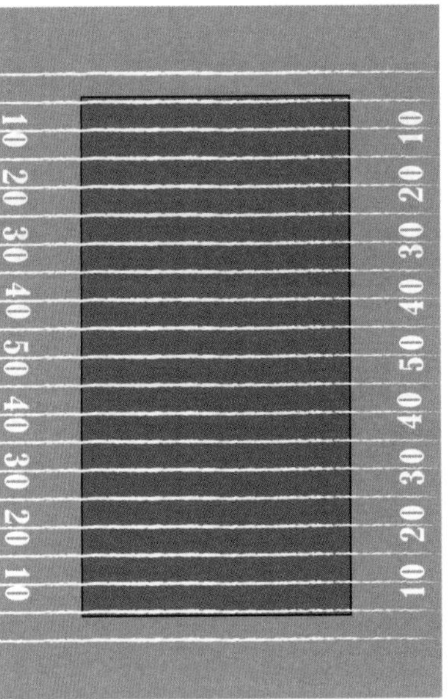

Farmer Frank was excited about winning the off-season football lottery. Winning the contest meant he would be able to use the local football field to grow crops in the off-season. He didn't need the whole field though, that was for sure. The entire field measured 360 feet by 160 feet. After much thought, Farmer Frank decided that he'd leave a 30 foot margin around all four sides of his planting area. With his mind made up, he started planting beets along the 50-yard line, carrots and beans along the 40-yard line, and watermelon along the 30-yard line. He finished off his crop by filling the rest of the planting space with corn. If Farmer Frank decided to build a fence around the portion of planted field, how many feet of fencing would he need to buy?

Challenge: The rug propped up between the old ping-pong table and the faded kayak at the yard sale was a thing of beauty. Sure, the edges were mostly frayed and there was one long stirp of binding trailing in the grass, but it had been years since Elsie had seen the elusive "small woodland animals playing badminton" pattern anywhere, and her cutting-edge designer sense told her it was about to make a big come-back. Since she had perfected the art of replacing rug bindings, she made her purchase and hurried back to her shop to lay the rug out on the floor and assess the damage. In her workroom which was 10 meters long and had an area of 50 square meters, Elsie straightened the rug and found that there was a 1 meter margin between each wall and all four edges of the carpet. How many meters of binding tape should Elsie buy to replace the binding on all four edges of the carpet?

A pig owner, a detective, and an accountant were sitting at a table in the accountant's office one day. They had a 1 liter bottle of water. They poured water from the bottle into a small rectangular container until it was full. If the small rectangular container measures 10 cm long by 5 cm wide by 5 cm tall, how much water is left in the bottle?

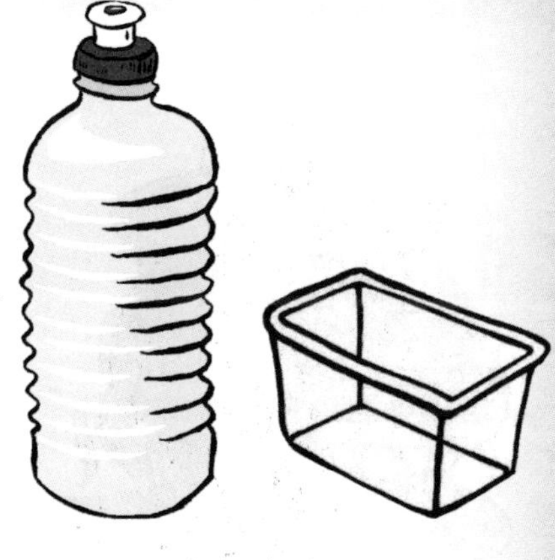

Volume = l x w x h

12

Hint: 1 L = 1000 cm^3

Practice Problem #1

Volume

Lord Elroy planted his foot firmly on the final step and heaved himself onto the ledge. He stared in wonder at the bubbling cauldron in front of him, knowing he didn't have much time. The flying squirrels would soon pick up his scent, and if the villagers of Pfuddyduddy were to have any chance at recovery from the Beriberi Plague, he would have to fill his rectangular, water-tight container with the healing waters of the Cauldron of Pfire quickly. As he pulled the custom-made piece of Supperware from his bag, he wondered if the 20 cm by 10 cm by 6 cm box would really hold enough Pfirewater to save all of the villagers. Quickly dismissing his doubts, he dipped the container in the cauldron, snapped on the lid, and beat a hasty retreat. How many liters of Pfirewater did the custom-made Supperware container hold?

Larry, the host of the Deep Fried Goodness Show, needed to clean out his deep fryer prior to filming this season's finale. The last episode had been a disaster. The remnants of his Fried Catfish Surprise had clung to his Deep Fried Flan like a dryer sheet to his favorite pair of stretchy pants, and now the fryer was a fishy, flan-y mess! Luckily, Larry had invented the oil change basket years ago. The 5-inch square basket was only 2.31 inches deep, but if you simply dipped it into the fryer, it would fill with oil that you could dispose of at the nearest Biohazard Reclamation Site. Refill with fresh oil and you're back in the deep frying business. How many cubic inches of oil does Larry's oil change basket hold?

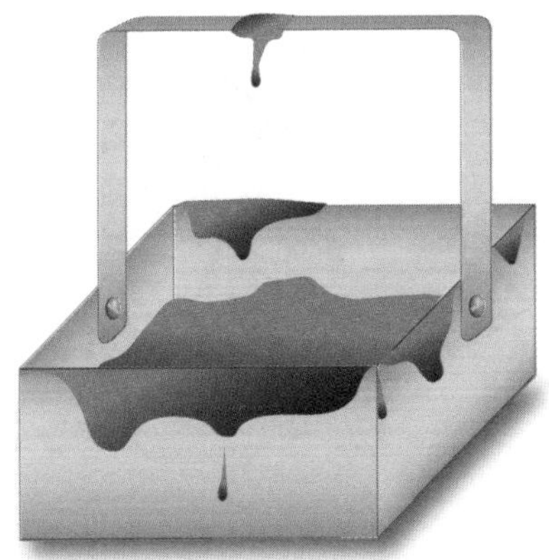

Practice Problem #3

Volume

Jackrabbit Hill was alive with the sounds of rushing water, canoe paddles slapping the water, and young rabbits laughing as they navigated the Hill's 8 creeks. One rabbit in particular was making a lot of noise. Simon Bigears had decided to attempt the first ever solo navigation of Carrot Creek—Jackrabbit Hill's longest and fiercest waterway. Simon let out squeal after squeal, as his canoe bopped up and down through the rapids. What a "hare"-raising adventure! In fact, Simon's canoe would probably sail right into the air if it weren't for the super-secret compartment he had designed in its hull. Measuring 1.5 m by 40 cm by 20 cm, the compartment held just enough water to serve as ballast to keep his canoe in the water and on track. How many liters of water did Simon's super-secret canoe compartment hold?

Hint: In order to calculate volume, all units of measurement must be the same!

To find out more about measurement equivalents, see the Units and Measurements section in the Tool Kit.

Pour Me

Volume

Practice Problem #4

Ben Beagle paced silently along the side of the pool. In his day, he had been quite the sprinter. He could doggie paddle the 30 meter length of the pool faster than anyone around. But that was then, and this is now. Today he walked the deck of the Canine Aquatic Temple (C.A.T.) as the new pool manager—the King of the C.A.T., the Poobah of the Pool. And today he knew that he needed to get water in the pool before sundown, or there would be some seriously disappointed puppies when the C.A.T. opened for the season tomorrow. Ben measured the width of the pool and then it's depth to find that both measured 10 meters. What is the volume of the pool in cubic centimeters? How many liters of water will Ben need to fill the pool?

12

Practice Problem #5

Trent Trout and his wife, Sally Salmon, were out shopping for a new home. They had given up the wild stream life years ago and, pooling their savings, they had purchased a beginner tank from a couple of catfish who were retiring to the coast. Now with their son, Little Bobby Bass, in the picture, their beginner tank was just too crowded. Since they both wanted a large family, they decided to take a tour of the XL GigaGlass model, which measured 10 m long by 6 m wide by 5 m deep. Although they both loved it, the XL model was just outside their budget. So they settled for the L model instead, which was the same depth as the XL but exactly 1 m shorter in both length and width. How many liters of water will they need to fill their new GigaGlass L model tank?

Limes for Sale

Carmelita Huevos bought 360 limes for $175.00. Since the temperature during rainy season had averaged 78 degrees Fahrenheit, the limes were 50% bigger than they were the last year. She packed the limes in small, green bags of 3 limes each. She gave them to her brother, Jose, and he sold all the bags of limes at $3.00 per bag. How much money did she make?

Practice Problem #1

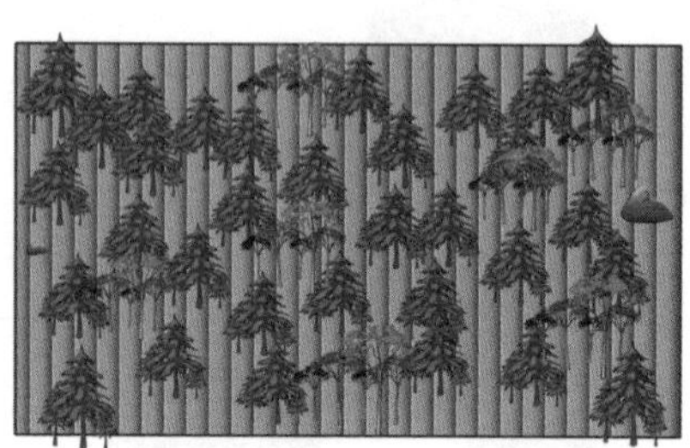

Akbar was starting to panic. When he had purchased the 120 acres of forest for the Big Project, he hadn't done his research. Now, the night before the Big Project broke ground, he finds out that 2/3 of the trees in the forest housed endangered pygmy flying squirrels, and he wouldn't be able to use them. Akbar knew that only 100 trees grew on each acre, and that this new development wouldn't leave him with enough trees. When his cell phone rang, he knew it was Big Jimmy calling to find out how many trucks he'd need to haul away the harvested trees. If Big Jimmy's trucks can carry 50 trees per truck, how many trucks will Akbar need to remove the trees he can cut down for the Big Project?

Limes for Sale

Multi-Step Problems

Practice Problem #2

It was finally the first sunny day Monty Chaney had seen in weeks. The sunshine meant that Paul, the owner of Four Burly Boys Concrete Company, would bring his crew to finish the concrete work around Monty's house. That day, Austin poured a patio slab that measured 10 yards by 30 yards, while his brother, Brian, poured a sidewalk that measured 30 yards by 2 yards. Out front, Adam finished the driveway which measured 15 yards by 18 yards. At the end of the day, Monty paid Paul $3,010 for the work, and Paul paid his workers $3 for each square yard of concrete that they poured. How much money did Paul have left over at the end of the day?

Hint: Sometimes it helps to start with the question and "think backward" through the facts to figure out what you need to know.

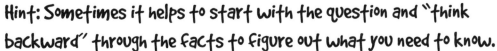

Limes for Sale

Practice Problem #3 **Multi-Step Problems**

Ben Beagle smiled contentedly as he reached for the bank's door. He had just wrapped up the most successful week in Canine Aquatic Temple (C.A.T.) history. On Monday, the C.A.T. had opened its doors at 8 a.m. By the end of the day, there had been a record 427 visitors! Tuesday through Friday had seen daily attendance decreases by exactly 12 visitors each day, compared to the previous day. With each visitor paying an entrance fee of $1.25, Ben Beagle had raked in an enormous amount of money. But unbeknownst to Ben, had just stepped into the middle of a bank robbery in progress. Five flying squirrels, wearing tunics made out of what appeared to be dish towels, stood at the counter, brandishing rubber-band guns. Once they saw Ben, the squirrels snatched the money from Ben's grasp, and exited the bank in a flash. If the squirrels split the money equally, how much would each squirrel receive?

13

Hint: A table can help you organize the information you know.

Day:	Number of Visitors:
Monday	
Tuesday	
Wednesday	
Thursday	
Friday	

Limes for Sale

Multi-Step Problems

Practice Problem #4

Old Man Jenkins waited impatiently by the mailbox. If it didn't come today, he would be in a pickle. That afternoon, the residents of Shady Acres would all gather at the local croquet field for the Biannual Crankypants Walk-a-thon. Old Man Jenkins' sponsors had promised that for every kilometer he walked today, he would earn $57 to put towards this year's Senility Ball. But if his new cane didn't arrive soon, he wouldn't be able to walk even one of the square croquet field's 125 m sides. Just as he thought all hope was lost, Babs' mail truck screeched to a halt in front of him, and she handed him a package from eBuy. The package measured 25 in by 5 in by 3 in and contained his fancy new cane! Arriving at the field in the nick of time, Old Man Jenkins walked at a brisk pace and circled the entire field 8 times before the walk ended. How much money did Old Man Jenkins earn for the Senility Ball?

Limes for Sale

The penguins at the Gubba Bump Fish Company were exhausted. The guy in the red suit was working their flippers to the cartilage. There were no happy feet on the ice that day, yet they persevered. The waddle of penguins diligently stuffed 10 fish in every box—no exceptions. At the end of the day, the guy in the red suit sailed away with a ship packed with 488 boxes of fish. He promised to sell as many individual fish as he could and send 3/8 of the proceeds back to the penguins. If the guy in the red suit sells 7/8 of the fish for $2 each, how much will the penguins earn for their hard labor?

Clem and Bobby Ray went fishing in the creek behind Old Man Jenkins' place. Clem caught 2 striped bass and 3 trout. Bobby caught 4 bluefin tuna. He also caught an electric eel. Since it was past 7:00 p.m. they fried up their catch for dinner. Clem just happened to have 2/3 of a quart of "Fried Right" cooking oil in the back of his 1972 El Cheapo. Bobby Ray suggested that it might be wise to save some of the oil for breakfast in the morning. So Clem used 3/7 of the oil to fry the fish. They ended up throwing the eel back in the creek. The next morning, Bobby Ray and Clem headed home to watch the 10:00 a.m. FASCAR race on TV. How much oil did Clem use to fry the fish the night they camped by the creek behind Old Man Jenkins' place?

14

As Clem and Bobby Ray settled into the couch for some serious FASCAR viewing, they discussed the ever-changing world of FASCAR politics. With 93 drivers on the FASCAR circuit, the competitive field was bigger than ever. For today's race, though, only 2/3 of the drivers qualified for the race. As the race was reaching its climax, Ernie Dalehard made a last-ditch effort to catch Stuart Tonay. But just as his car was moving faster than a buttered squirrel down an aluminum drain spout, he blew a tire, which led to a series of collisions. Thankfully, no drivers were injured, although the collisions did knock 1/2 of the drivers out of the race. What fraction of all of the drivers in the circuit finished the race? How many drivers were knocked out of the race?

Advanced Fractions: Products

Practice Problem #2

Bummed by the outcome of the FASCAR race, Clem and Bobby Ray decided to grab some snacks and head on down to the cement pond for some fun in the sun. Clem found 5/8 of a bag of Tater Chips behind the couch, and Bobby Ray still had half of a can of Academia nuts in the glove compartment of Clem's El Cheapo. Since they knew the cement around the pond would be warm, the good ole boys fashioned some flip flops out of work boots that had been run over by the lawn mower and 3 yards of string. After a quick dip, Clem and Bobby Ray had a snack and then a nap. If Clem ate 5/6 of the remaining Tater Chips, what fraction of the whole bag did he eat?

14

Practice Problem #3

Advanced Fractions: Products

Contrary to popular belief, Clem and Bobby Ray were a tad forgetful at times. And yep, they both neglected to apply sunscreen prior to their pool-side adventure, so that evening, both were sunburned like a couple of crispy critters. In fact, Clem and Bobby Ray sported two of the reddest necks you're likely to ever see. Needing to cool off in the shade the next day, they decided to go to the new release of "Alabama Jones and the Lost City of Tarnation." At the theater, Bobby Ray bought the 5-gallon Gutbuster Tub O' Popcorn, but since the Gutbuster came with free refills, he only saw about 4/5 of the movie on account of his numerous trips back to the snack bar. Due to the gastronomic consequences of his allergy to partially-hydrogenated coconut oil, Clem also spent a significant amount of time away from the big screen. In fact, he saw only 2/3 of what Bobby Ray saw. What fraction of the movie did Clem see?

Advanced Fractions: Products

Practice Problem #4

After the movie, Clem and Bobby Ray joined up with their friend, Earl, who had won four tickets to that night's tractor pull at the local fairgrounds. The tractor pull started promptly at half past seven. Crowd favorite "Crazy Jake" was driving his silver and cyan Dear Johan tractor. With 1,100 horsepower at his disposal, "Crazy Jake" managed to pull the sled 9/10 of the way to the finish line. Although "Crazy Jake" had set the bar high, newcomer Rascal Rollins felt up to the challenge. In his 1,200-horsepower Massive Fergeysohn tractor, Rascal put the pedal to the metal and very nearly won the competition. When the dust settled, though, Rascal had only pulled the sled 8/9 of the distance "Crazy Jake" had. What fraction of the track did Rascal Rollins pull the sled?

Practice Problem #5

After 3 non-stop hours of loud engines, Clem and Bobby Ray yearned for some peace and quiet. So, after dropping Earl off at the Podunk Laundromat, Clem and Bobby Ray headed over to the Barns & Yokel bookstore for a poetry reading. While neither of the two possessed any formal poetic training, they quite enjoyed hearing "pomes" that used funny words and rhymed. As luck would have it, tonight was limerick night, and Cooter, Enos, Elrod and Jed kept the laughs coming with original compositions about block engines, ground squirrels, bowling balls, and grits, respectively. Unfortunately, the fun came to a screeching halt when Professor Angie Lou from the local college took the stage and read an epic poem about gladiators…in Greek. Clem was distraught by the lack of rhyme and understood only about 2/3 of the words. Bobby Ray, despite being a fan of gladiators, only understood 2/7 of the words Clem understood. What fraction of the gladiator poem's words did Bobby Ray understand?

Shopping Spree

Advanced Fractions: Multi-Step Problems

Sample Problem

Granny and Gramps keep all of their money in their mattress. Lately, Gramps has been having some problems with his back which may have something to do with the hundreds of rolls of quarters on his side of the bed. They decided they had to spend that money as quickly as possible to save Gramps' back. At the mall, Gramps gave 2/3 of the money to Granny, so she could buy a Z-Box 180 and a big screen Plazmatic TV. Gramps spent 1/2 of the remaining money on a pedicure and a sea kelp facial. When they met back at the car, they still had $425.00 left in the trunk, which was way more than enough for breakfast at the We Wouldn't Steer You Wrong Steakhouse. How much money did Granny and Gramps have to start with?

15

Hint: What fraction of the money did Gramps give Granny?
So what fraction can you use to represent *all* of the money?
And then, what fraction remained?
What fraction of the remaining money did Gramps spend?
What was left over after that? ...which is equal to how much money?

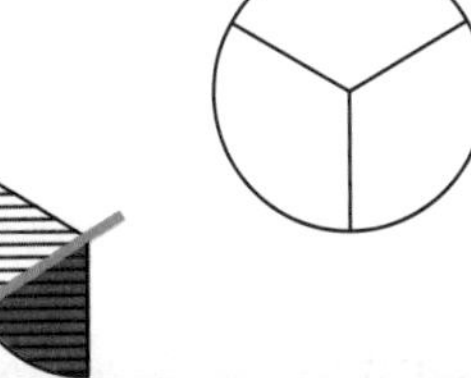

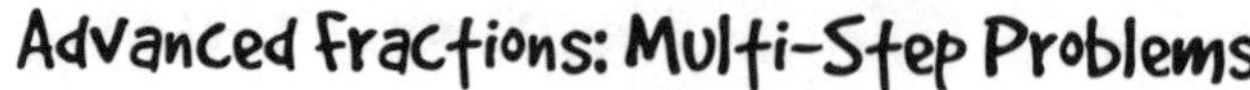

Practice Problem #1

Seth and Maggie could not believe they had spent the entire morning collecting golf balls. Seth thought the golfers at Cataract Country Club must be the worst golfers on the planet. Maggie agreed that they couldn't hit the broad side of a barn with a softball…let alone a golf ball. When they returned home, they sorted the golf balls they had found. Seth put 7/8 of the golf balls into a box on the upper shelf. Maggie took 1/3 of the remaining golf balls and put them in a basket to sell at their Lemonade/Used Golf Ball Stand, and left the rest in a bucket in the garage. Later that afternoon, Mary Ellen stopped by their stand for a glass of lemonade and some used golf balls. As luck would have it, she needed 6 golf balls and that's exactly how many golf balls Maggie had in her basket. How many golf balls total did Seth and Maggie find that day?

Hint: What fraction of the golf balls did Seth put in the closet?
So what fraction can you use to represent *all* of the golf balls?
And then, what fraction remained?
What fraction of the remaining golf balls did Maggie take?…which is equal to how many golf balls?
So then, if Maggie has so many golf balls (which equals a certain fraction), what fraction is equal to *all* of the golf balls?

Advanced Fractions: Multi-Step Problems

Practice Problem #2

Ella Funt was the smartest girl on her street. Her memory was simply amazing. To the astonishment of all the parents on Peanut Drive, she had successfully memorized all 24 license plates of the cars parked along both sides of the street. Mr. Bailey was so impressed that he awarded Ella a free afternoon at the zoo. Since they were her favorite animal, Ella planned to spend the last 3/4 of her time with the pachyderms, which meant she had to plan the rest of her time carefully. As soon as she got to the zoo, she spent 1/4 of the time before her pachyderm appointment with the monkeys. After the monkeys, she realized she still had 24 minutes before she was due at the Pachyderm Palace. How many minutes total did Ella plan to spend at the zoo?

Shopping Spree

Practice Problem #3

Luigi had never seen so much pepperoni. One little typo on the order form…that's all it took. And now here he was, knee-deep in pepperoni. Thinking quickly, he packaged up 5/6 of it and, with the help of a shoe horn and a logging chain, managed to get it in the freezer. Still faced with a mound of pepperoni on his front counter, Luigi decided to put 2/7 of what was left on the 40 pizzas about to leave the shop for the Alfresco wedding. When his brother, Donato, had finally left the shop with the wedding pizzas, Luigi took a deep breath and considered the 45 pounds of pepperoni still sitting on the counter. What could he do with it? He had no idea. All he knew was that he would never make such an ordering mistake again. How many pounds of pepperoni did he order in total?

Practice Problem #4

When the carrot harvest was complete, many of the rabbits wanted to throw a party to celebrate their great fortune. Peter, however, insisted that they work even harder to store as much of the harvest as possible for the lean winter months. Under Peter's constant heckling, the rabbits managed to store away 8/9 of the harvest in the form of carrot sticks, carrot juice, canned carrots, and delicious carrot cake. Proud of how hard they hard worked, Peter decided that they would cook 1/5 of the remaining carrots into a stew for a party that evening. As for the 88 pounds of leftover carrots, he divided them equally amongst the 11 rabbit families and sent them each home after the party with food for the next month. How many pounds of carrots in total did the rabbits harvest?

Practice Problem #5

Talk about irony. Vincent couldn't believe he'd spent 6/7 of his birthday money on the new Buzzer Blade 3750 remote control airplane, only to get it snagged in a tree during its inaugural flight. The unfortunate incident sent Vincent back to the hobby store where he ended up spending 1/4 of the remaining money on repairs. Now, here he sat, wondering if he should spend the $27 he had left on flying lessons. How much birthday money had Vincent received in total?

15

Every New Year's Eve, Aunt Mabel makes her "extra special" egg nog. Uncle Emmett brings his secret-recipe fruitcake. It is rumored (since it's a secret) that Uncle Emmett's fruitcake recipe calls for 3 cups of dates and 4 ounces of persimmons. Aunt Mabel's recipe, on the other hand, is actually posted on the bulletin board at the local Quik-E-Mart. In addition to the eggs, sugar, and nutmeg, you must carefully mix in 2 liters of buttermilk for every 7 liters of heavy cream. This year, Uncle Emmett made 2 fruitcakes. Not to be outdone, Aunt Mabel made an extra-large batch of egg nog. If she used 6 liters of buttermilk, how many liters of heavy cream did she need?

Recipe for Trouble

Old Man Jenkins won 3 tickets to the local taping of his favorite cooking show, "The Deep Fried Goodness Show." Since he owed them a debt of gratitude for fixing one of his canes, Old Man Jenkins decided to take Clem and Bobby Ray to the show. As luck would have it, Larry, the host, was cooking up something special today. With his demonstration table piled high with foot-long hot dogs, buttermilk, corn on the cob, tapioca pudding and water chestnuts, Larry could only be making one thing: his world-famous deep-fried foot-long tapioca corn-on-the-cob dogs! The boys, of course, were already salivating. As Larry began to cook, he explained that the key to the recipe was to use 4 cups of tapioca pudding for every 3 ears of corn. When all was said and fried, the platter Larry laid before the camera was a work of art. If Larry used two dozen ears of corn, how many cups of tapioca pudding must he have used?

Ratios

Practice Problem #2

The un-civil war between the primates and the pachyderms was getting out of hand. Jane, the zookeeper, was at her wits' end. Not only did the animals' monkey business upset the children visiting the zoo, but it was getting messy. For every 2 bananas the apes threw at the pachyderms, the elephants would return fire with a machine-gun like barrage of 37 peanuts. When you took into consideration the ice cream spilled by terrified children fleeing the scene, it's no surprise the battle ground between the two warring factions had become known as the "Banana Split." Now, after a long night of peace talks between the two enclosures, Jane thought she had finally made some progress, until just as she was turning away, first one banana, then another, whizzed by her head. If the monkeys opened the day with a volley of 22 bananas, the elephants would return fire with how many peanuts?

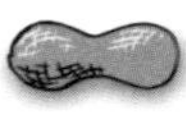

Practice Problem #3

Ratios

Jethro was proud of his new invention. Using only duct tape, the blades off of Clem's old lawnmower, and a hubcap from a Specific Motors sedan, Jethro had fashioned the world's first pizza cutter that could—with a solitary press on the Jethcut 2000—turn a pizza into 12 perfectly-symmetrical slices. Now, Jethro knew that most families (who only ate one or two pizzas at a time) wouldn't have use for a Jethcut 2000. But what about the institutions? Prisons, the old folks' homes, the schools, and other places with lots of inmates? Jethro believed those were the places where the efficiencies gained by using the Jethcut 2000 could make a real difference. To test his new product, he decided to give it a whirl at Shady Acres' weekly pizza day. Norm, Shady Acres' head chef, was a bit skeptical at first, but he soon became a believer as he witnessed Jethro turn 47 pizzas into how many perfectly-symmetrical slices?

When Cletus told Earlene they were going to honeymoon in Lost Bagels, she assumed they would be flying there immediately after the wedding. You can imagine her disappointment when Cletus, instead, had one of his buddies drive his dilapidated old Potomac Flytrap up to the front of City Hall. With about a hundred tin cans tied to the bumper, they hit the highway in a cacophony, backfires and screeching tires. What annoyed Earlene more than anything was that, every time they stopped for gas, Cletus had her get out and put more oil in the engine. The Flytrap's heyday—if it ever had one—was long gone and it now used 2 quarts of oil for every 40 gallons of gas. Three days and 280 gallons of gas later, the newlywed couple finally pulled into The Philly, the most-famous resort in Lost Bagels. Suddenly it didn't matter that Earlene had put how many quarts of oil into the Flytrap over the course of the trip?

Practice Problem #5

Ratios

The vendors at the 87th Annual Eastminister Dog Show were ecstatic. Attendance was the highest it had ever been in the show's history. And these pooches were hungry! Not surprisingly, Catsicles were outselling Squirrel Pops. In fact, the vendors were selling 5 Catsicles for every 3 Squirrel Pops. After "New Tricks for Old Dogs," the last seminar of the show, the vendors packed up their carts and totaled their sales for the weekend. All in all, the vendors had sold 129 Squirrel Pops. How many Catsicles had they sold?

The Cowtippers Organization of Washington (C.O.W.) had 724 members as of January 1, 2007. This represented a 43.2% increase over their 2006 membership numbers. The C.O.W. leadership attributes the skyrocketing membership numbers to a very successful advertising campaign sponsored by the Pork Is Great Society (P.I.G.S.). In April 2007, each member tipped exactly one cow. 137 members tipped a Jersey cow. 406 members tipped a Guernsey cow. The rest of the members tipped Polled Herefords. What percentage of the members tipped a Polled Hereford?

Hint: $\frac{\text{\# of something you'd like to know the \% for}}{\text{Total \# of something}} \times 100 = \_\_\_\%$

Practice Problem #1

Percentages

The smoke-filled room was filled with the usual sounds of dogs playing poker: chips clicking, tails wagging, growling, licking…you get the picture. This was the final round, so Rover decided to go all in. Scruffy and Scraps folded. That left Bruce. Calling Rover's bluff, Bruce also went all in. In total, there were 200 chips in the middle of the table. Scruffy and Scraps each had 25 chips in the pile. If Bruce had 70 chips in the pile, what percentage of the chips were Rover's?

Did you know... that "Dogs Playing Poker" actually refers to 16 oil paintings C.M. Coolidge completed in the early 1900s? Can you find out who asked him to paint them?

Practice Problem #2

Plaidbeard shook his head as he surveyed the deck of his ship. It had been a rough fortnight at sea. Of the 14 landlubbers he had hired to man his ship, two had succumbed to seasickness, and had been dropped off during their last raid. Three others had joined his new parrot in an attempted mutiny and had been forced to walk the plank. Adding insult to injury, two others had gotten into his private stash of gummy bears and had been swiftly thrown into the brig. So here he stood, captain of a skeleton crew of misfits, 1,000 miles from home. Oh, he knew that—if he ever made it home—this would make a whale of a pirate tale. But that was a big "if" at the moment. He did not like his chances. After all, he had only what percentage of his crew left?

Practice Problem #3 **Percentages**

Fog and Tad sat by the side of the stream, talking about their favorite things. Fog, of course, could speak at length about his button collection. With the addition of the three ivory buttons he had recently purchased at Scott the Skunk's swap meet, Fog now had a total of 1,250 buttons. Tad was floored. He could not believe Fog would spend so much money on buttons for his collection. Fog explained, though, that he hadn't spent money on most of them. For example, 625 of them had been gifts from his Aunt Mildred. In addition, 500 of his buttons had come from clothes his parents had given to him over his lifetime. Yes, he had purchased the remaining buttons in his collection, but that only amounted to what percentage of his collection?

Ronald the Raccoon was in the zone. Although he usually only hit 21 trash cans each week, it was getting toward the end of summer and that meant it was high time to start storing some food away for the winter. So, with that goal in mind, this week Ronald raided 50 trash cans. Ten of the trash cans were chock full of pizza left over from the Alfresco wedding. He also found 12 trash cans with leftover Squirrel Pops behind Eastminster Kennel Club. To date, though, the best find had to be the 8 trash cans full of pre-packaged Bran Nuggets he discovered behind Shady Acres. Although the remaining trash cans were devoid of good eats, Ronald had accumulated more than enough food for the foreseeable future. What percentage of the trash cans Ronald the Raccoon visited did not contain treats?

Practice Problem #5

Percentages

Geezer McDougall was in a real pickle. Here it was, the 15th of the month, and he was burning through his funds like he was made of money. Of course, he wasn't wealthy. Indeed, he was on a fixed income of $300 per month. His room and board at Shady Acres was $150 per month. When you figured he usually spent $90 per month on tuba lessons, that didn't leave a whole lot of discretionary income.* The last couple of weeks, he had taken each of the Dombrowski sisters on a date to the local cinema. Now he was almost broke. He sure wished that more than what percentage of his fixed income was discretionary?

***Discretionary income** is the money left after you've paid all of your bills that you can spend how you choose.

Mean Jumpers

Averages

Sample Problem

Hank, Rodney, and Mr. Jeepers were at the carnival one evening, when the barker challenged them to participate in a game of Hillbilly Hopscotch. Never one to back down, Hank stepped up right away. Rodney and Mr. Jeepers tried to slip away, but two large clowns forced them to Hank's side. Mr. Jeepers went first and then, Hank, emboldened by Mr. Jeepers' sudden burst of team spirit, sprang through the air like a jungle cat. Rodney, never one to be outdone by his friends, leaped forward like he was shot out of a cannon. The crowd cheered and much cotton candy was consumed forthwith. The average of all three jumps was 13 feet. If the average of Rodney's and Hank's jumps was 14.5 feet, how far did Mr. Jeepers jump?

Hint:

1. + | − ↑
2. ÷ | x

Practice Problem #1

Averages

Cletus had driven Earlene batty on their trip to Lost Bagels. Not only did he have to add oil every time they stopped for gas, but Cletus also made her keep an eagle eye out for the cheapest gas. He kept saying they had to stay within budget if they were going to be able to afford the More-Than-You-Should-Eat Buffet. For example, as they traveled through Alabammy, they had to stop for gas three times. On average, they ended up paying $3.67 per gallon for gas there. Their first stop had been in Mobeel, where they paid $3.73 per gallon. From there, they made it all the way to Montgumry, where they paid $3.70 per gallon. Earlene had earned her spot at the buffet, though when they passed through Tuskaloosey and she noticed a Quick-E Mart selling gas for how much?

Averages

Practice Problem #2

A tear ran down Percival's cheek as the Yellowhound bus passed the "Now Leaving San Berdu" sign on the outskirts of town. His time in San Berdu had been clam-tastic, but he understood that all good things must come to an end. When the fickle climate changes of El Dino caused the price of a bucket of clams at the Clam Pit to hit $20, he knew it was time to move on. Not knowing exactly when his next meal would be once he left town, Percival had decided to make his last week in San Berdu one to remember. On Monday, Wednesday and Friday, he had eaten an average of 75 clams each day. On Tuesday and Thursday, which were always half-price clam days, he had eaten an average of 125 clams each day. Taking into consideration all five days he ate clams, how many clams on average did Percival eat each day?

Practice Problem #3

Buoyed by last season's championship victory, Bubba's Holy Rollers rollerpolo team started the new season on fire. Indeed, their righteous mallets connected on every strike and left their opponents in shambles. Over the course of their first three games, the Holy Rollers averaged 14 goals per game. In the first two games—a doubleheader against the Salon Sweepers—the Holy Rollers averaged 10 goals per game. But then, in just their third game of the season, the Holy Rollers faced their arch-nemesis, the Rusty Buckets, in a grudge match repeat of last season's championship. With the Rusty-Bucket-intimidation-factor no longer a threat, the Holy Rollers—fueled by nine years of pent-up frustration—steamrolled their opponent, scoring how many goals in a lopsided shutout victory?

Averages

Practice Problem #4

Bruce stared across the stream with a lump in his throat. He knew the magnitude of the challenge before him. It was time for his beaver crew to show what they were made of. If they were going to complete this dam on time, they would need to average 100 feet of new construction every day for the next five days. Bruce knew they could do it, but a little encouragement would probably help. Reaching into his gig bag, Bruce pulled out his electric ukulele and plugged it into his battery-powered amp. He strummed a few chords and then launched into a rousing rendition of "100 bottles of Juice on the Dam." Enlivened by Bruce's ukulele playing, the beaver crew averaged 110 feet of new construction each day for the first four days. Proud of his crew's efforts, Bruce told them that they would likely be able to finish early on the last day. How many more feet of new construction was left to complete the final day?

The Dombrowski sisters had struck gold. In an effort to repair some of Shady Acres' exercise equipment before this year's Senility Ball, the sisters had been scouring magazines for the perfect fundraiser…and they'd finally found it: the Curmudgeon 5000. Not only was it a telephone that would also wake the user in time to do those all-important things, like taking medication and getting to the restaurant in time for the Early Bird Special, it also came with "whippersnapper" features, such as auto-emailing children and grandchildren when they hadn't visited for X number of days. To reach their goal, the sisters needed to sell an average of 20 Curmudgeon 5000s per day for the next six days, and so far, the residents of Shady Acres snapped them up like bran flakes. Over the first four days, the sisters sold an average of 25 units each day. For each of the final two days, how many units do they need to sell on average to meet their goal?

FASCAR racing teams are always pushing the limits of technology in their unending pursuit of speed. FASCAR driver Gordon Jeffers is using a corn-based racing fuel. He can now drive 120 km on 12L of "Gas on the Cob." Ernie Dalehard, on the other hand, is experimenting with a new fuel distilled from cooking oils. Using "French Fry Fuel," Ernie is able to travel 90km on 10L of fuel. Perhaps most impressive, though, is Stewart Tonay's mixture of guava juice, lima beans, and oatmeal—combined with the battery power of 4,762 "AAA" batteries. This enables Stewart to drive an astounding 150km on only 5L. How far can Gordon Jeffers travel on 15L of "Gas on the Cob"? How much "French Fry Fuel" will Ernie Dalehard use if he travels 54km?

Fuel for Thought

Practice Problem #1

Ben Thayer got a brand-new lawnmower for his 16th birthday. It wasn't exactly the set of wheels he had been hoping for, but his parents wanted him to put it to good use making money for college. Ben's best friend, Doug Thatt, got a used lawnmower for his birthday just two weeks later. Since Ben's mower was new, he could mow 4 lawns with a full, 2-gallon tank of gas. Doug's mower, on the other hand, was 3 years older than Ben's and could only mow 3 lawns with a full, 2-gallon tank of gas. If Ben Thayer and Doug Thatt go into business together and evenly split a 10-gallon can of gas, how many lawns will they be able to mow together?

Rates

Practice Problem #2

Wayne Bruce was tired of life as a secret superhero. Not only were his superhero duties starting to put a damper on his social calendar, they were also starting to put a serious dent in his wallet. The Wombatmobile could only travel 12 miles on a full, 24-gallon tank of gas—a fact that had never concerned Wayne until he had bought his new, day-job commuter vehicle, the Gasmizer Deluxe. Unlike the Wombatmobile, the Gasmizer Deluxe could travel an astounding 320 miles on a full, 8-gallon tank of gas. Wayne's dilemma reached a climax when the Wombat Signal sounded, alerting him to a problem in Tunnelton—960 miles away. He knew he'd probably miss the features of his superhero car, but he cringed at the thought of how much gas it would take to drive the Wombatmobile all the way to Tunnelton. What a conundrum! How much gas would Wayne need if he drove the Wombatmobile to Tunnelton? How much gas would he need if he drove the Gasmizer Deluxe instead?

Practice Problem #3

As a college student, Professor Stodgypants had done his dissertation on the comparative slithering capabilities of the Fang Viper and the common snail. His careful observations had revealed that a Fang Viper could cover 95 meters in 5 seconds. The common snail, on the other hand, took 15 minutes to cover the same amount of ground. Little did he know that his research would one day save his life. One fateful Saturday morning, while he was trimming his prize petunias, he heard the tell-tale (or is that tell-tail?) rattle of a Fang Viper. Slowly turning, he spotted the snake aggressively coiled approximately 133 meters away. His mind raced as he computed how long it would take him to reach the safety of his garden shed, which stood directly behind him. As he leapt toward the shed, a huge smile spread across his face, for he knew he could make it there in 6 seconds—and that it would take the Fang Viper how long to travel the 133 meters to his current position?

Practice Problem #4

Eileen had beaten the odds and she had the aluminum medal to show for it. Ever since she was 13 years old, she had loved running, but it was not easy for her. You see, she had one leg that was 4 centimeters shorter than the other. Despite this physical limitation, Eileen kept at it and eventually broke records, running an amazing 120 meters in only 12 seconds during the state championship race. Her win at the state level meant that she would compete at Nationals next month in San Berdu. At the national level, however, the race would cover 180 meters, which was the international standard. If Eileen maintains her state championship pace, how long will it take her to run the 180-meter national championship race?

Practice Problem #5

Rates

Since Bobby Ray had gone to Tuskaloosey for the holiday weekend, Clem called Dutch to see if he wanted to come over to watch FASCAR on TV. Dutch got all excited and said he'd be over in two shakes of a dog's tail. That satisfied Clem, who looked around his place and decided it was not quite ready for guests yet. Mainly, he knew he needed to secure grape soda. Usually, Clem would drink a six-pack of grape soda over the course of a 3-hour FASCAR race. He also knew that Dutch had a reputation for being able to drink a cool dozen grape sodas during a race. Well, this weekend was the 24-hour FASCAR marathon, and that meant that Clem needed more grape soda—a lot of it, actually. In fact, he was completely out of grape soda presently. If Clem runs to the store, how many (individual) grape sodas does he need to buy to last Dutch and himself the entire FASCAR marathon?

At the FASCAR concession stand, a small popcorn costs $\$x$. A Super Mega Jumbo soda pop costs three times as much as a small popcorn. A FASCAR "value" meal, which consists of a Carburetor Chicken sandwich, Tire Tread fries, and a Super Mega Jumbo soda pop, costs $8 more than a Super Mega Jumbo soda pop alone. If the FASCAR "value" meal costs $14, how much would it cost to buy a small popcorn and a Super Mega Jumbo soda pop?

20

Practice Problem #1 **Algebra**

Lord Sudsbury's day had turned out better than expected. The Duchess of Winch, who was in town visiting his wife, had insisted that he go skeet shooting with her brother, the Earl of Hurl. Lord Sudsbury knew what she was up to, of course—the frightful woman missed nary a chance to embarrass him. Since the Earl of Hurl had won the Tewksberry Club championship three years running, Lord Sudsbury knew the Duchess was looking forward to a full report of his sound defeat. Unbeknownst to her, however, Lord Sudsbury had been practicing in anticipation for this very day. The Earl of Hurl, who ended up hitting x targets that day, was blown away by Lord Sudsbury's shooting prowess, as he hit 3 times the number of targets as the Earl. When the gun smoke finally cleared, the two sportsmen had hit a total of 24 targets that day. Later, when the Duchess pressed for details of who had hit how many targets, how did Lord Sudsbury proudly reply?

Diligently following the advice of their expensive P.R. consultant, the three billy goats Gruff were working hard to overcome their bad reputations. If any of them hoped to be elected to the Field council, they'd need to convince the locals that they were more than rude, bearded, tin-can-eating ruffians. So, after a good shave and more than a little dental work, the three billy goats Gruff hit the pavement in search of paws to shake and babies to kiss. William, the eldest, headed straight to Flor Mart where he stationed himself by the entrance and successfully greeted x customers. Will, the middle brother, found a nice spot by the local watering hole and greeted 5 more individuals than his older brother. Pedro, the youngest, went to Barns & Yokel, which was packed due to the release of the latest Hairy Otter book, and managed to greet 9 more Field residents than William. If the three goats greeted a total of 74 residents, how many residents did each Gruff greet individually?

Snack Time

Practice Problem #3

Algebra

As the annual Ocho de Mayo celebration had been rained out yesterday, the townsfolk decided to go ahead with the festivities tonight, since the sky was clear. Luke would, of course, try to defend his title as King Burrito, but something about celebrating Nueve de Mayo didn't sit right with him. The extra day had allowed a dark-horse European contender to enter the fray. In fact, the local news reported that Taco Johan had just arrived on a cruise liner from Denmark. Luckily, Luke had continued to fast last night, anticipating that the contest would be rescheduled for today. Miz Chalupa, on the other hand, had gone to the More-Than-You-Should-Eat Buffet. As a result, tonight she was only able to wolf down x burritos. Taco Johan, still feeling the effects of seasickness, was only able to eat 2 more burritos than Miz Chalupa. All of this worked in Luke's favor, and "Ol' Iron Stomach" managed to put away 11 more burritos than Taco Johan. If the contestants ate 90 burritos all together, how many did each contestant eat individually?

The feud between the flying squirrels, the beagles and the badgers hit a fever pitch in the summer of '74. It had all started when the flying squirrels mocked the beagles for being afraid to ride The Whipporwill, the largest roller coaster in the amusement park. In response, the beagles challenged the squirrels to a roller coaster ride-off, and before long, it became a 3-way battle. Of course, the wily badgers' craftiness soon became apparent. The flying squirrels and the beagles kept losing their place in line to various and sundry badger tricks, including the ol' buttered squirrel gag and the occasional cry of "Fetch!" When the park finally closed, the flying squirrels had ridden The Whipporwill x times, and the beagles, who were a little less easily fooled, had ridden the coaster twice as often as the squirrels. As nobody had distracted the badgers from the game, they rode the coaster an impressive three times more than the flying squirrels. If all three groups rode the coaster a total of 42 times all together, how many times did each group ride individually?

Practice Problem #5

Algebra

The pig, the chicken and the sheep met at the diner for dinner last Tuesday night. Out of respect for their fellow dinner guests—and to help make this barnyard word problem "udderly ridiculous"—they didn't order bacon, eggs or lamb chops. Instead, they each ordered the tofu plate. However, the chicken, who was never a big fan of tofu anyway, only pecked around her plate and ate only x pieces of tofu. The sheep, unbeknownst to the others, had just started a low-soy diet, yet still managed to eat 7 more pieces of tofu than the chicken had eaten. The pig, true to his form, finished his plate as well as the leftovers from the others, for a grand total of 3 times the amount of tofu as the chicken. If the chicken, the pig and the sheep ate a total of 47 pieces of tofu altogether, how many pieces of tofu did each eat individually?

Speed

Sample Problem

Ernie Dalehard left Daytona Beach at 9:45 a.m. With his windows rolled down, he sang Mason-Dixon Chicken songs at the top of his lungs. Since he had plenty of beef jerky in the glove box and a Super Mega Jumbo soda pop in the cup holder, he did not have to make any stops until he reached the final destination in Miami at 2:15 p.m. The trip computer on his car computed his average speed on the trip as 95 km/hr. Based on Ernie's trip data, how far apart are Daytona Beach and Miami?

$$\text{Speed} = \frac{\text{Distance}}{\text{Time}}$$

Hint: In order to use the formula for speed, you will need to know how many hours he drove . . .

Road Trip

Practice Problem #1

Barry McGuire, the '70s solo artist who recorded the hit album "Bullfrogs and Butterflies," had to get to Kalamazoo to launch his third farewell tour by 7 p.m. tonight. He glanced at his watch and grimaced. It was already 12:45. If he were going to make it to the concert on time, he'd need to cover the 30 miles between Chicken Junction and Kalamazoo in a hurry. Thankfully, he'd just tuned up his Harley Mo-ped. He quickly loaded his trusty old guitar into the kid trailer attached to the back, and coasted down the driveway at 1 p.m. How fast would he need to travel—on average—to make it to the concert on time?

Speed

Practice Problem #2

Lulabelle and Bessy were on the lam. At 10:15 a.m., they had hijacked the Udderly Fantastic milk truck and hit the road looking for adventure. They soon found it, as two local policemen on motorcycles gave chase. While Lulabelle drove the milk truck through a series of evasive maneuvers, Bessy threw 8 glass bottles of milk onto the pavement behind the truck, creating a minefield of glass shards that soon deflated both policemen's tires. Confident that they would now make a clean getaway, the bovine bandits put the pedal to the metal and headed due south. Lulabelle and Bessy maintained an average speed of 90 km/hr. They figured they'd be safe as soon as they reached at Granny Bossy's farm, 360 km away from the scene of the crime. At approximately what time will these cows-gone-bad reach Granny's farm?

Practice Problem #3

Yoga Bear and his lil' buddy, Bubbaloo, set off into the wilderness at promptly 6 a.m. They went in search of the Golden Pikanik Basket, which they believed they would find at the base of Mount Smoky, approximately 16 miles away. At 2 p.m., they reached Mount Smoky, only to find newly-constructed condominiums and a beaver lodge. Disappointed and hungry, the bears sat down to rest, since they were also tired from maintaining a grueling pace of what speed throughout the forest on their journey?

21

Speed

Practice Problem #4

The train chugged steadily along the track. It had left Cellulite Station with its cargo of three-dozen Thighblaster 4000s at 7:30 a.m. Traveling at only 20 miles per hour through the Hefty Mountains, it was due in Saggy Bottom at 8 p.m. How far is it between Cellulite Station and Saggy Bottom?

Practice Problem #5

Challenge! Roscoe and Rita were on the run. The all-camp game of Capture the Flag was getting intense, and these two camp veterans had just snatched the flag from the hollow of a tree down by the creek. Finalizing their plans to divide and conquer, Rita dashed off due west with flag tucked into the pocket of her hoodie—all except the required "5 inches of visibility," that is. Roscoe watched her go, and then turned and ran due east for 10 minutes at 600 feet per minute. Unfortunately, Rita was tagged after running for only 8 minutes at 500 feet per minute. How many feet will Roscoe have to run back (to the west) to recapture the flag from where Rita was tagged?

Gordon and Horatio could not believe that they had water duty the first day at camp. There were 27 scouts in their troop, so they would need to refill the bucket 5 times that day. At the well, they used a jug to fill the bucket. After emptying 20 jugs of water into the bucket, it was 5/8 full. Gordon dumped another 8 jugs into the bucket and then the jug slipped out of his hand and into the well. Luckily, Horatio had a cup with him. After 10 cups, the bucket was finally full. The boys lugged the bucket of water back down the hill. Gordon told the camp director that he had lost the jug down the well and the camp director replied, "you'll just have to use that cup from now on." How many cups will the bucket hold?

Practice Problem #1

After winning the door prize at this year's Senility Ball, Old Man Jenkins decided to treat the residents of Shady Acres to some free bagels. He hobbled down to Beagle's Bagels and asked for as many bagels as his fixed income would allow. The girl with pink hair behind the counter filled a large box full of bagels and sent Old Man Jenkins on his way. When he got to Shady Acres and opened the box, he saw that 1/4 of the bagels were sesame. There were also 48 more cinnamon bagels than sesame bagels. The remaining 152 bagels were plain. How many bagels were there altogether?

Water Torture

Advanced Fractions: Division

Practice Problem #2

Bobby Jo spent 2/5 of his weekly take-home pay on video games for his Z-Box 180, and 1/2 of the remainder he used on a Thighblaster 4000. He spent $12 more on the video games than he spent on the Thighblaster 4000. How much money (after taxes) does Bobby Jo make each week?

22

Did you know? When a company pays you for your work, they first take out *income tax* (and a few other taxes) to pay to the government. The rest you receive in your paycheck as *take-home pay*. So your salary = taxes + take-home pay. The money Bobby Jo spent is from his take-home pay.

Practice Problem #3

Hillary and John were running against one another for class president. Hillary earned 1/4 of the votes while John earned 1/3 of the votes. The winner of the election, however, turned out to be a write-in candidate named Russ Parole, who won with a total of 45 votes. If Hillary, John and Russ were the only 3 candidates, how many votes were cast altogether? How many votes each did Hillary and John receive?

Water Torture

Advanced Fractions: Division **Practice Problem #4**

Duke read 2/5 of his ice cream truck repair manual on Monday. On Tuesday, he read another 420 pages. If Duke still has 1/2 of the ice cream truck repair manual to read, how many pages total are there in the book?

When Vince turned 16 this past Saturday, he took all $422 in his savings account and bought a used 1975 Hi-Way Croozer. He got such a good deal on it because the gas gauge is broken and the dealer did not know how large the gas tank was. With the help of his Uncle Cooter, Vince set about the task of determining how much gas the Croozer would hold. Thanks to Uncle Cooter's home-made 'T'aint Full Yet device, the fellas determined that the tank was 1/5 full when they began their experiment. Vince grabbed his can of gas and, after adding 7 gallons to the tank, the tank was now 2/3 full. Vince said, "Eureka! I've got it!" How many gallons will the Croozer's tank hold?

22

Heavy Thinkers

Sample Problem

Private Sanders, Wendy, and Mr. McDonald were all headed to the 49th floor of the Fast Food Administration. They wished to share an elevator, but a sign in the elevator read: "Maximum Capacity: 100 kg." They compared weights and were astounded to learn that Private Sanders weighed twice as much as Mr. McDonald. Wendy weighed only 4 kg less than Private Sanders. The average of their weights was 32 kg. Can they all safely ride the elevator together? How much does each person weigh?

Practice Problem #1

Mr. Whitherby, Sammy, and a guy everyone just called The Conductor met at El Huevo Loco for 2-for-1 burrito night. Although they had intended simply to have a quick snack before catching a matinee of "The Chalupa Always Rings Twice," the trio of friends would soon be responsible for eating 2/3 of the 90 burritos served that evening at El Huevo Loco. It all started when The Conductor bet Mr. Witherby that he could eat the most burritos. Sammy quickly jumped into the fray and before long, belts were being loosened and burritos were being devoured like juicy gossip at the water cooler. The Conductor made good on his bet, eating twice as many burritos as Mr. Witherby. Sammy ate 4 more burritos than Mr. Witherby, despite the fact that this was his first experience with a mass ingestion contest. How many burritos did each amigo eat?

Algebra Challenges

Practice Problem #2

The aardvarks were so close. They could see the lights of Lost Bagels shimmering in the distance ahead. Their trip across the desert had been an arduous one, yet they had managed to cover an average of 12.5 miles per day over the four days of the trip. The first day had been the hardest. The hot sun was so oppressing that they had managed only x miles that day. The following day, however, was cloudy and they covered twice as many miles as the first day. On the third day, it rained but they still managed to travel 2 more miles than they had on the previous day. And then, today, with Lost Bagels on the horizon, they had given it their all and cranked out 4 more miles than the day before. How many miles did the aardvarks travel altogether? How many miles did they travel each day?

23

Practice Problem #3

Their first morning at Camp Pinecone, the Snickerdoodle girls had been distraught to find that their favorite Capture the Flag battle grounds had been decimated by last summer's forest fire, and the whole area needed to be replanted. To spur the camp into action, Kelly's cabin renamed themselves the Mongoose Horde, and challenged the other cabins to a tree-planting competition. One thing led to another, and by the time the forest floor settled, the girls at Camp Pinecone had planted 3/4 of the camp's 4,360 pinecones in the burned-out area. The Woodchucks had planted a total of X pinecones. The Platypus Clan's tag-team approach helped them plant three times as many pinecones as the Woodchucks. But the Mongoose Horde's automatic 'cone catapult had launched twice the number of pinecones as the Platypus Clan into prime planting space. How many pinecones had the girls planted altogether? How many pinecones did each cabin plant?

23

Heavy Thinkers

Practice Problem #4

Thelma, Bertha, Velma and Dominique drove to Vern's Seaworthy Crafts to rent a boat to celebrate their graduation from beauty school. Vern warned the ladies that his boats had a strict weight limit of 500 pounds—even one pound over and the boat would sink to the bottom like a lead balloon. Slightly offended by Vern's insinuation, the ladies plopped their money down on the counter, grabbed life vests, and headed for the nearest boat. On the way to the docks, Thelma, who weighed 3 pounds more than Bertha, told the others that they would show that mean ol' Vern a thing or two about beauty-school graduates and sailing. Velma, who weighed 10 pounds less than Thelma, sniffed loudly and glared in Vern's general direction. Only Dominique, who weighed 7 pounds less than Velma seemed concerned about Vern's warning. If the average weight of the four friends was 130 pounds, what will happen when the sailing beauties board ship? How much does each lady weigh?

Practice Problem #5

There was once an old lady who lived in a shoe. It was a used size-7 athletic sneaker and smelled something awful. It was also quite cramped since the old lady had 3 kids living with her. After winning the 50/50 raffle at a local football game, the old lady met with a local realtor, who helped her move up to a brand spankin' new size 13 mountain boot. The kids, whose average shoe size was an 8, were ecstatic. Little Toeny, who had the smallest feet, loved to slide down the laces of his new house. His older brother, Archie, who wore shoes two sizes larger than Little Toeny, loved to play with their dog, Bunion, and he often tried to teach Bunion to heel. The eldest child, Naillie, had the largest feet of all—a full two sizes larger than Archie. Naillie was quite straight-laced and would never, ever stick out her tongue. If the old lady spends the rest of her raffle winnings on new shoes for the three kids, what size should she purchase for each?

23

A detective spent 1/6 of his money on a Mason-Dixon Chickens CD. He spent 3/5 of the remainder on overpriced coffee drinks that he can't even pronounce. If the coffee cost $11 more than the CD, how much money did he spend altogether?

Chicks 'n Beans

Luke stepped out onto the balcony of his hotel room. There, hundreds of feet below him, the waves of the Specific Ocean lapped at the sandy shore. Luke took a deep breath. He loved the smell of the salt in the air and—could it be? Yes, he was sure it was. Somewhere down below there was a burrito vendor. Grabbing his wallet, he headed to the elevator with a smile on his face and a rumble in his tummy. On the street, the smell of refried beans and cheese was much stronger. Like a bloodhound, Luke caught the trail and was soon standing before the beach-side burrito vendor. He spent 3/4 of his money on 3 Burrito Locos and 6 Chalupas Grandes. When he was finished, he was still hungry. The Chalupas Grandes had been more delicious than he ever could have imagined. If a Burrito Loco costs 3 times as much as a Chalupa Grande, how many Chalupa Grandes could Luke buy with the rest of his money?

24

Fraction Challenges

Practice Problem #2

When Vladimir parted ways with Mrs. Witt, he spent 1/5 of his money on a cab ride into town. Since he was still a little embarrassed about that incident with the spray cheese in the local convenience store, Vlad (that's what his friends call him) spent 1/2 of the remainder an ingenious disguise, which consisted of a large red handkerchief, a clown nose, a puffy shirt, sandals and knee socks. When he looked in his wallet, he realized he had exactly $14 left, which would be just enough for the Early Bird Special at the Cow Palace. How much money did Vladimir have to start with?

Practice Problem #3

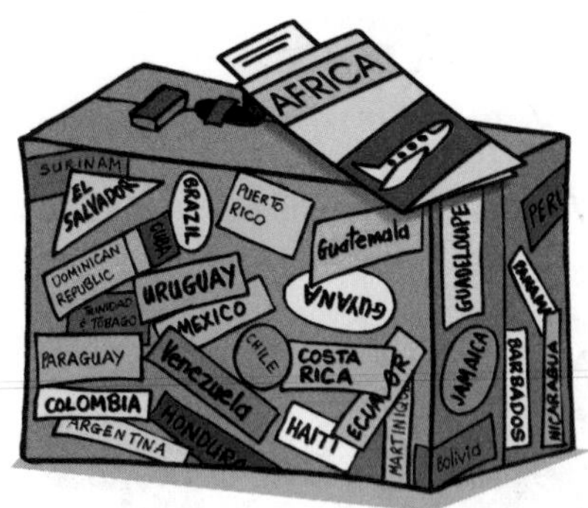

Professor Stodgypants had finally saved up enough money to go on his dream trip to Africa. At long last he would finally be able to study the rare African Bolin Constrictor in its natural habitat. Upon arrival in Port Squeezy, Professor Stodgypants was delighted to find that food and lodging was much less expensive than he had feared. In fact, he only spent 1/3 of his money during the first week of his stay. After the novelty of the area had worn off, he spent even less—only 1/5—of his money in the second week. If he spent $1,600 altogether, how much money did he have total in his vacation fund?

24

Fraction Challenges

Practice Problem #4

Johan Sebastian Guttenberg knew the end was near. His solo trip to the Equator had been a miserable failure, in his opinion. Despite careful reference of his 27 full-color maps, he could not for the life of him find the Equator line on the ground anywhere. Although he looked high and low (mainly low, obviously), he still couldn't find it. Moreover, he had just recently been stricken with a severe case of scurvy. Or was it rickets? He couldn't be sure. All he knew was that his skin had turned a putrid shade of plaid and his profuse sweating had left him dehydrated. In his final moments of clear thinking, he used a pen made out of a coconut to write a Last Will and Testament on a piece of bleached monkey-hide. His last wishes were for all his possessions to be sold, with 3/5 of the money going to his wife and the remainder divided equally between his 4 offspring. If, after his inevitable demise, his children each receive $800, how much will his wife receive?

Practice Problem #5

Fraction Challenges

Jethro could scarcely believe his eyes. There, in his hands, was a letter from the largest venture capital firm in all of Podunk. The letter said they wanted to invest—heavily—in the Jethcut 2000. He could hardly contain his excitement. The things that this would mean: no more late rent payments, an overhaul for his '67 Croozer, and maybe—just maybe—a bit of cosmetic dental work. He wasted nary a minute getting to work—which meant hitting up Podunk's garage sales for the raw materials he would need. Jethro grabbed the milk can from behind the velvet picture of Stanley the Singing Frog and emptied its contents into his trouser pocket. At Bobby Ray's garage sale, Jethro hit the mother lode. He spent 3/5 of his money on 6 hubcaps and 8 lawn-mower blades. He figured that with the rest of his money he could buy another 12 hubcaps. However, if he spends all of the rest of his money on lawn mower blades only, how many lawn mower blades can he buy?

24

Lil' Johnny took his dad's fishing tackle box to school for show-and-tell yesterday. Aside from the fact that Lil' Johnny is now grounded from varmint hunting for a full week, his presentation to his class was a great success. His classmates were particularly interested in the many fishing lures his dad has. The kids counted and discovered that 1/5 of the lures in the tackle box were purple. The remaining lures were either orange or green. The ratio of the number of orange lures to the number of green lures was 2:3. If there were 12 green lures in the tackle box, how many purple lures were there?

Bait and Switch

Practice Problem #1

Bubbly Betty, Blondie and Blind Barb were biding their time by the bayou before bopping into Boonieville's next Balloon Bashing Bout. Each of the bodacious beauties was burdened with a basic task to ensure their next bout went off with, well…a bang. The bulk of their round went as planned and before long, Betty's band had beat the opposition and won not only the trophy but prize money as well. Bubbly Betty, Blondie and Blind Barb decided to split the bucks in a ratio of 6:5:3, respectively. If Blondie's cut is $45, how much money in total did they win?

Practice Problem #2

A moose and a beaver were reclining next to a stream. As they were debating the relative merits of hunting vs. gathering, they heard an odd tinkling sound coming from the stream. When they sat up to investigate, they were amazed to see a steady stream of bottles of Uncle Geezer's Old Tyme Root Beer floating lazily down the stream. Every so often, the bottles would collide with each other and small stones in the stream, making an extraordinarily enjoyable tinkling sound. The moose and the beaver quickly waded into the stream and began to collect the bottles of root beer. Since he was bigger, the moose retrieved more bottles than the beaver in a ratio of 7:5. If there were 72 bottles total in the stream, how many more bottles did the moose retrieve than the beaver?

Practice Problem #3

Kentuckiana Jones tossed his pencil and protractor aside and raised his map in frustration. “Blast these trigonometric roadblocks!” he shouted. “I’ll never find the Lost City of Phuntabulous at this rate.” On the verge of giving up, KJ noticed a peculiar shape taking form on his map as he held it up to the light. There, hidden beneath layers of dirt and grime, was what he had been searching for: the key to the map! It resembled a triangle, the length of whose sides were in a ratio of 4:3:5. Using his slide rule, tweezers, and an old popsicle stick, KJ determined that the perimeter of the triangle measured 48 cm. KJ knew that the shortest side of the triangle represented the most direct route to the Lost City, so he needed to find out how long that shortest side was. What is the length of the shortest side of the map scale triangle?

KJ rejoiced when he discovered that he is currently at one end of the triangle’s shortest side. If the map’s scale ratio is 1 cm : 5 mi, how many miles away is the Lost City?

Bait and Switch

Ever since their trip to Lost Bagels, Cletus and Earlene have enjoyed collecting funny bumper stickers. Cletus' favorite is the one that says "Hard Work Never Killed Anyone BUT WHY TAKE THE CHANCE?" Earlene prefers the one that says "What if the Hokey Pokey *is* what it's all about?" Recently, they've been engaged in a bit of competitive collecting to see who can find the funniest bumper stickers. The ratio of the number of Cletus' bumper stickers to the number of Earlene's bumper stickers is currently 5:2. Cletus has 27 more bumper stickers than Earlene. How many bumper stickers should Cletus give to Earlene so that the ratio of the number of his bumper stickers to her bumper stickers will be 3:4?

Bait and Switch

Practice Problem #5

To get in shape for bass fishin' season, Clem and Bobby Ray have embarked upon an ambitious new diet and exercise program. First, they no longer use the TV remote. If they want to change the channel, they take turns getting off the couch to change it manually. Second, they only eat donuts without sprinkles. Finally, and most importantly, they no longer go back for thirds (or fourths or fifths) at the More Than You Should Eat Buffet. As of this morning's weigh-in, 1/6 of Clem's weight is equal to 1/9 of Bobby Ray's weight. What is the ratio of Clem's weight to Bobby Ray's weight?

On January 1, 2007, the Pork Is Great Society (P.I.G.S.) had 1200 members, 60% of which were cows and 40% of which were chickens. During Fair Week, the P.I.G.S. executed a very successful New Member Campaign, which resulted in the addition of 400 new members. After the new P.I.G.S. members were sworn in during a secret ceremony, President-elect Bo Vine noted that the percentage of members who were cows had fallen to 50%. How many of the new P.I.G.S. members sworn in during the secret ceremony after Fair Week were cows?

Practice Problem #1

Jethro was excited, finally, to be selling his Jethcut 2000 door-to-door. This morning, his plan was to visit the Dombrowski sisters at Shady Acres and then head on over to Moneytree Lane to try to sell as many units as possible. As luck would have it, each of the two Dombrowski sisters wanted her own Jethcut 2000. Since they were his first customers of the day, he sold them each one Jethcut 2000 at only 10% over cost. When he hit Moneytree Lane, though, the money really started rolling in. By lunchtime, he had sold an additional three units, each at 35% over cost. If Jethro received $1,875 from his sales, what is the cost price of a Jethcut 2000?

Percentage Challenges

Practice Problem #2

The fans at the FASCAR track were on their feet. It was the last race and it had come down to a dogfight between Ernie Dalehard and Stewart Tonay. Since all of the other drivers had fallen by the wayside, all the fans in the stands had split their support between the two frontrunners. 60% of the fans were cheering for Stewart Tonay, and there were 250 more Stewart Tonay fans than Ernie Dalehard fans. How many fans total were at the race?

Practice Problem #3

Percentage Challenges

On his first day on the job as "The Guy Who Puts the Clowns in the Tiny Car," Bo Jest crammed 24 clowns into the tiny car. As you may have read about in the news, however, there was a bit of an accident (minor wardrobe damage, nothing serious, mind you) that occurred when the clowns exploded from the tiny car like a roman candle on the 4th of July. Not to be deterred by such a minor setback, Bo redoubled his efforts. After a significant amount of research on the latest space-age lubricants, Bo returned to the circus the following day and, after a litany of promises and a few bribes, managed to fit a whopping 36 clowns into the tiny car without incident. What percent more clowns did Bo Jest fit into the tiny car today than yesterday?

26

Percentage Challenges

Practice Problem #4

Delbert was really frustrated. The ol' paycheck just didn't go as far as it used to. For example, he cashed his check today and immediately had to spend 10% of his pay on diapers for Maude. As if that weren't enough, he then had to spend 20% of the remainder on tutus for Katarina and Isabella. When he looked into his wallet, Delbert could hardly believe that he only had what percentage of his pay left?

Practice Problem #5

Just Say NO! to Negativity!

National Spel Spellling Bee Ruan Runer-Up

Cletus and Earlene's bumper sticker collection had grown to enormous proportions in the last couple of months. Out of all the new additions to his collection, Cletus thought the best was the one that read "Just say NO to negativity." Earlene's most recent favorite was the one that read "National Spellling Bee Runer-Up." Altogether, the two now had a total of 500 bumper stickers. Earlene now has 24% more bumper stickers than Cletus. Cletus thinks its unfair that Earlene now has how many more bumper stickers than he has?

26

Speed Challenges

Sample Problem

On the day of his most famous bank robbery, Smitty Werben Jaeger Man Jensen took $723.47 from the vault in the Tumblewood bank. Smitty stole the fastest horse he could find, a noble steed named Frank and headed south, hoping to make it to the border town of Cactopolis before nightfall. It took 6 hours to cover the first 3/4 of his trip at an average of 12 mi/hr on his stolen steed. Somewhere around Thunderfhoof, his money bag ripped and 2/3 of the coins fell out. Fearing that there might be a posse in pursuit, Smitty refused to stop for the fallen loot. Instead, he hightailed it the rest of the way to Cactopolis, and arrived at exactly 6:00 p.m. If Smitty averaged 18 mi/hr during the last 1/4 of his trip, what time did he leave Tumblewood?

Hint:

$S = \frac{D}{T}$

$T \times S = D$

$T = \frac{D}{S}$

Practice Problem #1

Angelique and Dusty both drove a distance of 240 miles from their home in Ramal to the airport in Louisville. Given the price of gas, Dusty thought driving separately was a waste, but Angelique insisted it was necessary because she still had to get a pedicure. As a result, Angelique started her trip one hour later than Dusty. However, due to her lead foot and the massive engine in her Urban Suburban, Angelique actually reached the airport at the exact same time Dusty did. If Angelique's average speed was 80 miles per hour, what was Dusty's average speed?

Speed Challenges

Practice Problem #2

Back on shore again, Plaidbeard the Pirate piled his crew into his new Minibus XL and drove them 80 miles from the docks to Parrotopolis to have lunch at China Buffet. For the first 40 minutes of the trip, Plaidbeard drove an average speed of 75 miles per hour. But then he saw a policeman on a motorcycle and thought it best to slow down just a bit. The rest of the way to China Buffet, he drove at an average speed of 72 miles per hour. If Plaidbeard and his crew left the docks at high noon, what time did they arrive at Parrotopolis?

Horse Thief

Practice Problem #3

After the FASCAR season was over, Ernie Dalehard invited Stuart Tonay to go camping. Unbeknownst to Stewart, Ernie had modified the engine in his RV so he could make the 180 km drive to the campground faster than Stewart. Despite Ernie's souped-up RV—and the fact that Stewart ended up leaving town 40 minutes after Ernie—Stewart's superior driving skills (and the inherent superiority of his Specific Motors RV) got him to the campground a full 20 minutes before Ernie. If Ernie Dalehard's average speed in his modified RV was 60 km/hr, what was Stewart Tonay's average speed?

27

Speed Challenges

Practice Problem #4

On their first anniversary, Cletus and Earlene drove back to Lost Bagels to relive their honeymoon. On the way there, they averaged 30 miles per hour over the course of the 210-mile trip. As they were packing to go home, they suddenly remembered the new season of The Deep Fried Goodness Show would start that night. So, in order to make it home in time for the early airing, Cletus put the pedal to the metal and averaged 70 miles per hour on the return trip. What was their average speed for the whole trip?

Hint: To find the total average speed... average $S = \dfrac{\text{total } D}{\text{total } T}$

Practice Problem #5

Speed Challenges

At high noon, Ethan jumped on his Hogley Favoriteson motorcycle and began the 40 mile journey from Frogtown to Podunk. At the exact same time, Noah mounted his trusty steed, Buttercup, and left Podunk and heads toward Frogtown. If Ethan travels at 30 miles per hour and Noah squeezes 6 miles per hour out of Buttercup, how far apart will they be at 12:30 p.m.?

Tool Kit

Tool Kit

This page intentionally left blank.

Tool Kit

Clue Words

Addition Clue Words

adds	added	additional	altogether
together	bought	more	more than
sum	includes	how many	in all
total	increased by	combined	both
	all	another	

Subtraction Clue Words

decreased by	minus	less	difference between
difference of	more than	less than	
how much more	left	remain	fewer than
take away	only	higher	remains
words that end in -er:	faster	heavier	larger
longer	slower	farther	shorter

Multiplication Clue Words

of	times	multiplied by
product of	increased by	decreased by
factor of	every	at this rate
in all	total	each
doubled	tripled	quadrupled

Division Clue Words

each	equal	equally
evenly	per	separate
a	ratio	ratio of
quotient	quotient of	percent

Tool Kit

Simple Steps to Solve Word Problems

1. **Identify the question.** It may help you to underline the question(s) in red.
2. **Eliminate the irrelevant information.** With a *pencil,* ~~cross out~~ information that you don't think relates to the question. If you find you need the information again later, you can simply erase and retrieve.
3. **Highlight useful information.** Use a highlighter to mark numbers or phrases that relate to the question. If you're uncertain, you can use a yellow colored pencil until you feel more confident.
4. **Identify clue words.** Underline clue words in blue.
5. **Put it all together, and solve!** Remember, if you get stuck, we'll walk you through the sample problem on the DVD, or you can see how we marked up each problem in the Answer Key.

Here's a sample word problem after we've marked it up:

Once Amber Waves and her beloved Polly Esther were reunited after the Word Puzzler's trickery, Amber Waves decided they needed a day of relaxation at the Spa. ~~They left for the spa at 9:00 a.m. in order to fit in some sunbathing time at the pool around 3:00 p.m.~~ That morning, Amber Waves enjoyed a $25 egg plant facial and a $30 manicure, while Polly Esther spent all her time in a perfumed mud bath for $40. Fortunately, mid-mud-bath, Polly Esther remembered that she had just received a birthday check from Grandpa Hammie for $100. What was the total bill for their combined Spa treatments? Did these two relaxing beauties have enough money to pay for their day at the Spa?

$25
$30
+ $40
$95 total

$100
- $95
$5

Yes, they had enough money.

Units, Measurements and Conversions

Unit Conversions in the Metric System

In order to understand the metric system, you need to understand its structure. Just like our integer (whole number or counting) system, the metric system also works with groups of 10.

In the same way we count units, tens and hundreds, the metric system uses prefixes to designate these different quantities.

The prefixes on the staircase are used with all units of measurement in the metric system—length (meters), volume (liters), and mass (grams). But to help you understand how these prefixes work, let's say our made-up base unit of measurement is "widgets".

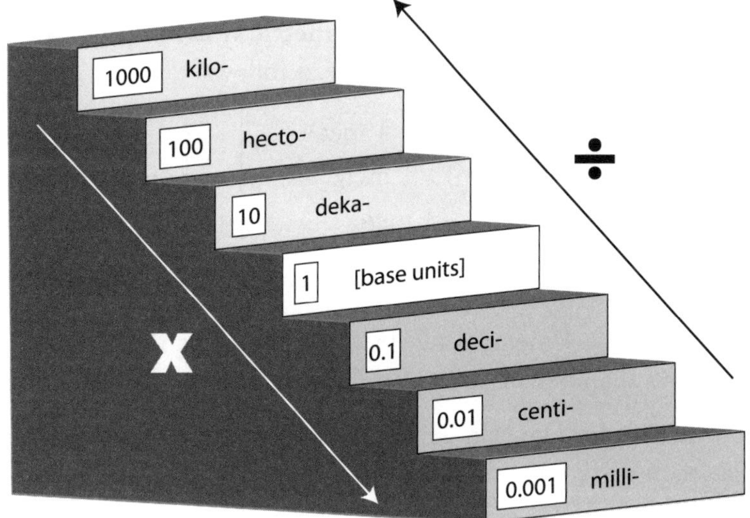

If you have 3 widgets, you're using the base unit "widgets" to measure the quantity.

If you have 10 widgets, you can also say you have 1 "**deka**widget," because *deka-* means 10.

If you have 100 widgets, you can also say you have 1 "**hecto**widget," because *hecto-* means 100.

If you have 1000 widgets, you can also say you have 1 "**kilo**widget," because *kilo-* means 1000.

If you have 0.01 widgets, you can also say you have 1 "**centi**widget," because *centi-* means one hundredth.

If you have 0.001 widgets, you can also say you have 1 "**milli**widget," because *milli-* means one thousandth.

On the other hand: if you have 100 centiwidgets, you also have 1 widget.

To convert from one unit to another on our staircase, you have to consider which direction you're moving.

Say you have **6 kilowidgets**, and you want to know the equivalent value in **widgets**. Since you're converting from a larger unit to a smaller unit (moving down the staircase), you'll multiply by:

$10^{\text{[the number of steps you have to move]}}$

In this case, we move down 3 steps from *kilo-* to base units, so we multiply 6 by 10^3 or (10 x 10 x 10). So:

$6 \times 10^3 = 6 \times (10 \times 10 \times 10) = 6 \times 1000 = 6000$

Which means: 6 kilowidgets = 6000 widgets

Now let's try it with more common units. How many meters are equal to 8,000 cm? (To move up the staircase, divide by $10^{\text{[the number of steps you have to move]}}$.)

In this case, we move up 2 steps from *centi-* to base units, so we divide 8,000 by 10^2 or (10 x 10). So:

$8{,}000 \div 10^2 = 8{,}000 \div (10 \times 10) = 8{,}000 \div 100 = 80$

Which means: 8,000 centimeters = 80 meters

Units, Measurements and Conversions

Length

The standard unit of length in the **metric system** is the *meter* (m). Other units of length and their equivalents to 1 meter are as follows:

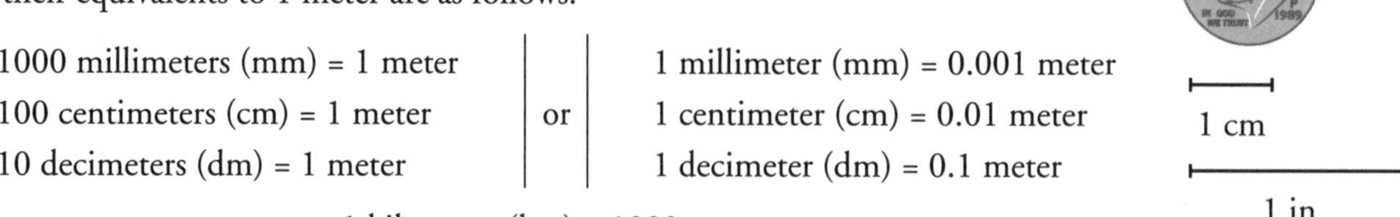

1000 millimeters (mm) = 1 meter | or | 1 millimeter (mm) = 0.001 meter

100 centimeters (cm) = 1 meter | or | 1 centimeter (cm) = 0.01 meter

10 decimeters (dm) = 1 meter | or | 1 decimeter (dm) = 0.1 meter

1 kilometer (km) = 1000 meters

1 cm

1 in

For reference, 1 meter is a little longer than 1 yard or 3 feet. A centimeter is nearly the diameter of a dime, a little less than half an inch. A millimeter is about the thickness of a dime.

In the **standard system**, length is measured by the *foot* (ft).This sheet of paper is about 11 inches tall—a little less than one foot.

1 ft. = 12 inches

1 yard = 3 ft.

1 mile = 5,280 ft.

To convert from Standard to Metric:

If you know...		Multiply by:	To find...	
in	inches	25.4	millimeters	mm
ft	feet	0.305	meters	m
yd	yards	0.914	meters	m
mi	miles	1.61	kilometers	km

To convert from Metric to Standard:

If you know...		Multiply by:	To find...	
mm	millimeters	0.039	inches	in
m	meters	3.28	feet	ft
m	meters	1.09	yards	yd
km	kilometers	0.621	miles	mi

To convert units within a system of measurement:

How many inches are in 4 feet? | 1 ft = 12 in | 60 inches are equal to how many feet?

1. **Create a fraction** with information from the question.

   $\frac{4\text{ ft}}{1}$

2. **Create a fraction with the equivalent you know.** Set it up so when you multiply, the units will cancel.

   $\frac{4\text{ ft}}{1}$ $\frac{12\text{ in}}{1\text{ ft}}$

3. **Multiply.**

   $\frac{4\cancel{\text{ft}}}{1} \times \frac{12\text{ in}}{1\cancel{\text{ft}}} = 4 \times 12\text{ in} = 48\text{ in}$

---

1. **Create a fraction...**

   $\frac{60\text{ in}}{1}$

2. **Create a fraction with the equivalent you know.**

   $\frac{60\text{ in}}{1}$ $\frac{1\text{ft}}{12\text{ in}}$

3. **Multiply.**

   $\frac{60\cancel{\text{in}}}{1} \times \frac{1\text{ ft}}{12\cancel{\text{in}}} = \frac{60}{12}\text{ ft} = 5\text{ ft}$

Tool Kit

Units, Measurements and Conversions

Volume

The standard unit of volume in the **metric system** is the *liter* (L or l)[1]. One liter is equal to 1000 cubic centimeters in volume. Other units of volume and their equivalent to 1 liter are as follows:

$1 \text{ L} = 1000 \text{ cm}^3$

1000 milliliters (mL) = 1 liter		1 milliliter (mL) = 0.001 liter
100 centiliters (cL) = 1 liter	or	1 centiliter (cL) = 0.01 liter
10 deciliters (dL) = 1 liter		1 deciliter (dL) = 0.1 liter

1 kiloliter (kL) = 1000 liters

From these units, we see that 1000 milliliters equal 1 liter; so 1 milliliter equals 1 cubic centimeter in volume. For reference, 1 liter is a little more than 1 quart. One teaspoon equals about 5 milliliters.

In the **standard system**, volume is measured by the *gallon* (gal.).

1 gal. = 4 quarts (qt.)

1 quart = 2 pints (pt.)

1 pint = 2 cups (cp.)

To convert between systems:					
If you know...		Multiply by:	To find...	
gal.	gallons	3.785	liters	L
L	liters	0.264	gallons	gal.

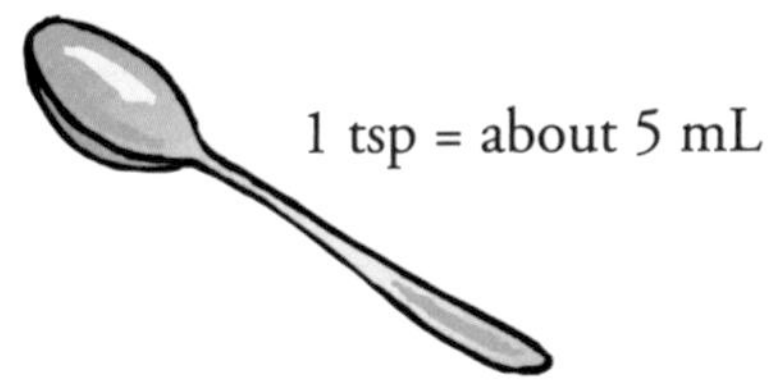

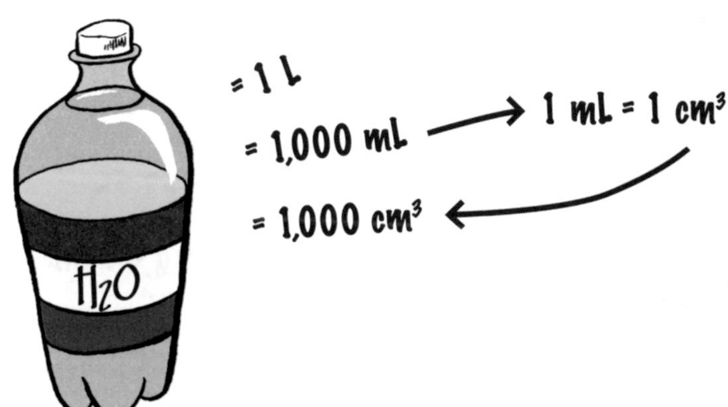

1. Did you know that both the lowercase *l* and the uppercase *L* are accepted abbreviations for liters? However, to avoid confusion with the number 1, we'll use the abbreviation L throughout this program.

Units, Measurements and Conversions

Mass

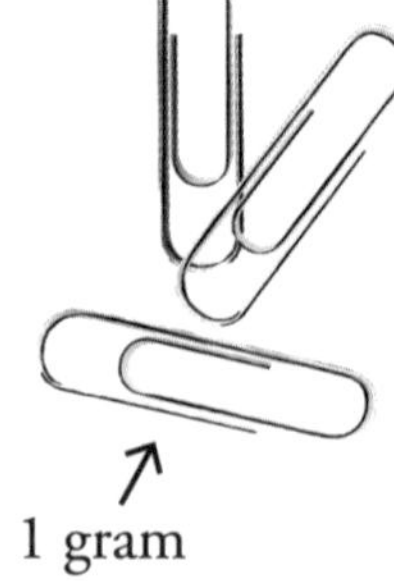

The standard unit of mass in the **metric system** is the *gram* (g). Other units of mass and their equivalent to 1 gram are as follows:

1000 milligrams (mg) = 1 gram		1 milligram (mg) = 0.001 gram
100 centgrams (cg) = 1 gram	or	1 centigram (cg) = 0.01 gram
10 decigrams (dg) = 1 grams		1 decigram (dg) = 0.1 gram

1 kilogram (kg) = 1000 grams

For reference, 1 gram is about the mass of a paperclip. One kilogram is about the mass of a liter of water.

In the **standard system**, pounds (lb.) are used.

1 pound = 16 ounces (oz.)

1 ton = 2,000 pounds

To convert between systems:				
If you know…		**Multiply by:**	**To find…**	
oz	ounces	28.35	grams	g
lb	pounds	0.454	kilograms	kg
g	grams	0.035	ounces	oz
kg	kilograms	2.202	pounds	lb

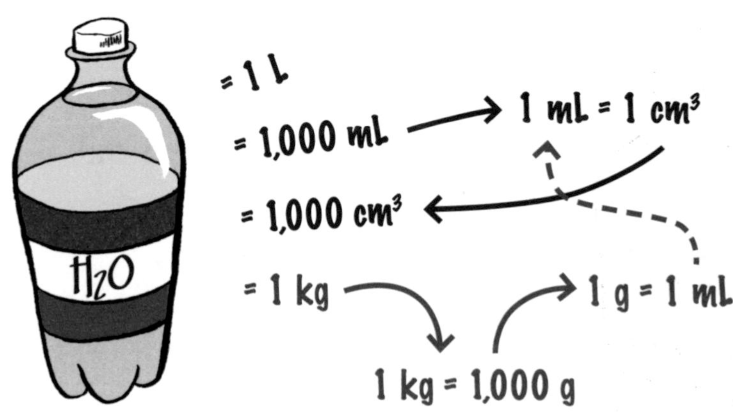

Tool Kit

Units, Measurements and Conversions

Time

Use following conversions when working with time:

1 minute = 60 seconds
1 hour = 60 minutes = 3,600 seconds
1 day = 24 hours
1 week = 7 days
1 year = 365 days
1 decade = 10 years
1 century = 100 years

Once Upon a Time…

A **fortnight** is 14 days.

Abraham Lincoln's Gettysburg Address begins…

"Four score and seven years ago…"

A **score** is 20 years.

So "four score and seven years" is how many years?

4 x 20 + 7 = 87 years

Temperature

Temperature is expressed in degrees Celsius in the **metric system**. In the **standard system**, degrees Fahrenheit are used.

The boiling point of water (at sea level) is:

100° Celsius (100° C) or 212° Fahrenheit (212° F)

The freezing point of water (at seal level) is:

0° Celsius (0° C) or 32° Fahrenheit (32° F)

To convert between systems:		
If you know…	**Multiply by:**	**To find…**
°F Fahrenheit	(F – 32) x $\frac{5}{9}$ or (F – 32) x 1.8	Celsius °C
°C Celsius	1.8C + 32	Fahrenheit °F

Tool Kit

Common Formulas

Key:	P = Perimeter	C = Circumference	A = Area	V = Volume
	b = base	d = diameter	h = height	l = length
	r = radius	w = width		$\pi = 3.1416\ldots$

Perimeter

Perimeter is the total length of all sides of a shape.

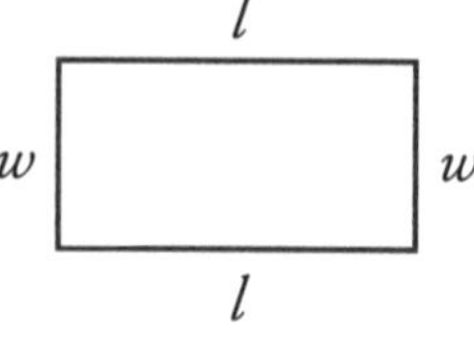

Rectangle: $P = l + l + w + w$ or $P = 2(l) + 2(w)$

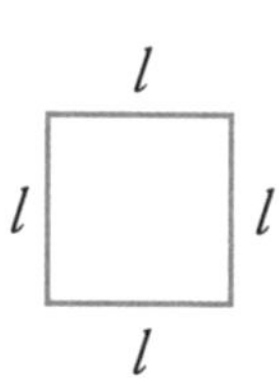

Square: $P = l + l + l + l$ or $P = 4(l)$

Triangle: $P = l + l + l$

Circle:* $C = \pi d$

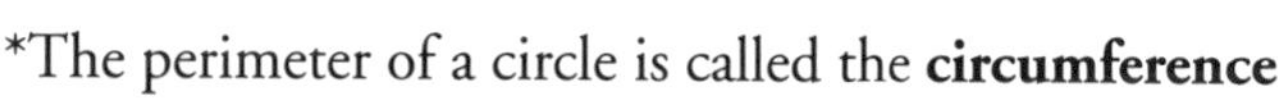

*The perimeter of a circle is called the **circumference**.

Area

Area is the number of square units (x^2) needed to cover a surface.

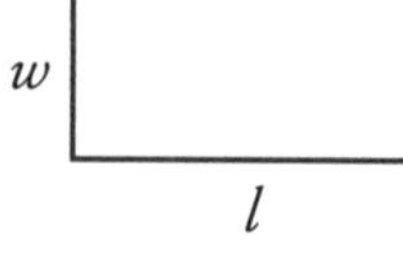

Rectangle: $A = l \text{ x } w$

Square: $A = l \text{ x } l$ or $A = l^2$

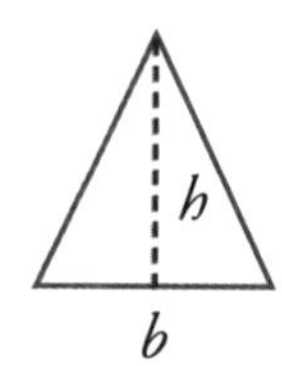

Triangle: $A = \frac{1}{2} b \text{ x } h$ or $A = \frac{b \text{ x } h}{2}$

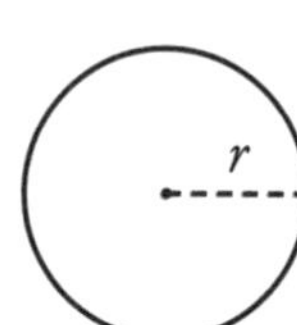

Circle: $A = \pi r^2$

Volume

Volume is the amount of space occupied by a three-dimensional object, and is measured in cubic units (x^2).

Rectangular prism: $V = l \text{ x } w \text{ x } h$

Cube: $V = l \text{ x } l \text{ x } l$ or $V = l^3$

Sphere: $V = \frac{4\pi r^2}{3}$

Cylinder: $V = \pi r^2 \text{ x h}$

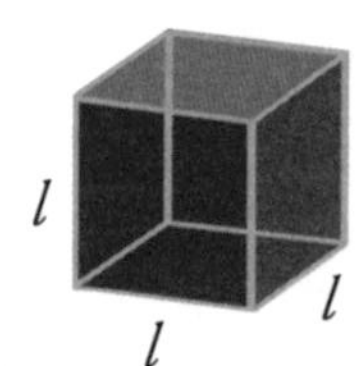

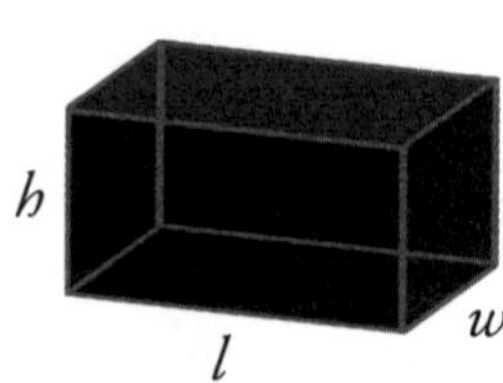

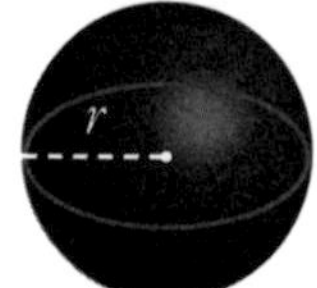

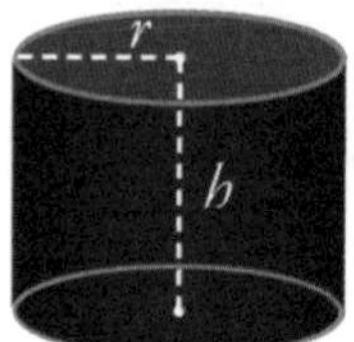

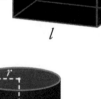

Answer Key Rebus Solution

[world] – L

The **Word**

[puzzle] + r

Puzzler

can

[knot]

not

stump

[ewe]

you!

[grate]

Great

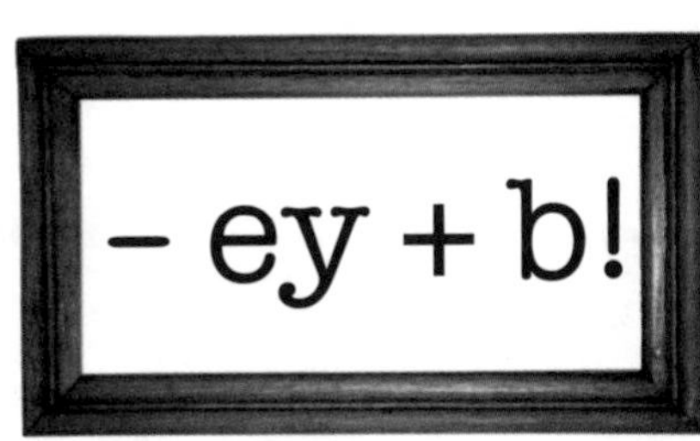

[joey] – ey + b

job!

This page intentionally left blank.

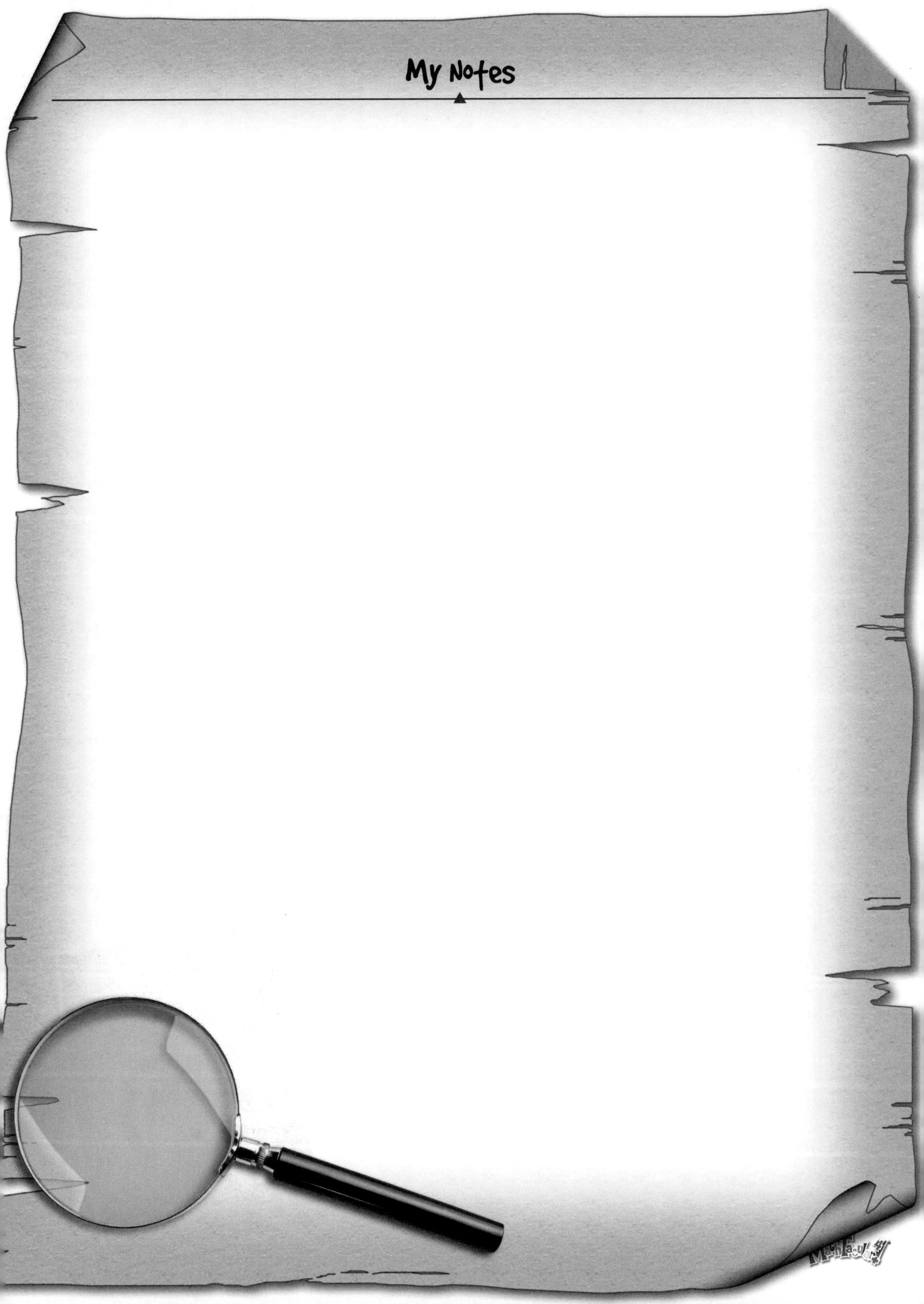
My Notes

My Notes

My Notes

Just Say NO! to Negativity!

My Notes